Handling the
media

Communication
and presentation
skills for healthcare
professionals

John Illman

First published worldwide in 2016 by

JIC Books
9 Grand Avenue
London N10 3AY
England

www.jicmedia.org

A CIP catalogue record for this book is available from the
British Library

ISBN 9780993517808

Printed and bound in Great Britain by CPI Antony Rowe, Chippenham

Contents

The author 8

With thanks 9

Acknowledgments 11

Introduction 12

Chapter 1 Journalists 15

Chapter 2 The news business. What makes news? 28

Chapter 3 Responding to a media interview request 39

Chapter 4 Preparing for a media interview 53

Chapter 5 Different types of interview 65

Chapter 6 Making an impression 73

Chapter 7 Writing for the media 91

Chapter 8 Social media and blogging 109

Chapter 9 Presenting to the media and other audiences 129

Chapter 10 Media case histories. A suitable case for treatment 146

Chapter 11 Narrative medicine. Keep taking the words 163

Chapter 12 Medicine and the media: 1950-2000. A brief history 171

Epilogue 180

Further reading 181

Index 182

To Liz, James and Chris

"Things should be made as simple as possible, but no simpler"

(Attributed to Albert Einstein)

The author

John Illman is a media and presentation skills trainer and a communications consultant. His career includes five years in London as medical correspondent on the *Daily Mail*; eight years as health editor on *The Guardian*; and three years as medical correspondent on *The Observer*. Founder editor of *New Psychiatry* and a former editor of *GP*, he was also a *Woman* magazine columnist and, for six years, chair of the Medical Journalists' Association.

A visiting tutor at the University of Westminster, London, since 1999, he helped to pioneer Europe's first BA (Hons) Medical Journalism course for medical students. He co-ran a communication course for science postgraduate students at the University of Cambridge for eight years. John started his career in the theatre at the Nottingham Playhouse and with the New Southwold Repertory Company - experience he finds invaluable in presentation skills training.

He has won many awards, both as a journalist and author, and has more than 300 broadcast credits. His reports include *The Expert Patient*, *Pathways to the Mind* (with Malcolm Lader); *Masks and Mirrors of Mental Illness*; and *Medical Advances and Animal Research*. Books include *The Body Machine* (1981) with heart transplant pioneer Christian Barnard; *Use your brain to beat Depression* (2004); *Use your brain to beat Panic and Anxiety* (2005); *Beat Panic and Anxiety* (2006); and *Animal Research in Medicine: 100 years of Politics, Protest and Progress. The Story of the Research Defence Society* (2008).

With thanks

I have always felt committed to how I have made a living. This is as true now as when I drew my first pay cheque after making my professional stage debut. My unlikely journey from the theatre to medical journalism owes much to those who invested their faith in me – they gave me the experience to write this book. They include the late Andre van Gyseghem, then director of productions at Nottingham Playhouse and my first communications coach; my first local newspaper editor, the late Roy Lomas; Robert Wallace, then publisher of *New Psychiatry*; Graeme Andrews, Oliver Gillie and Jerry Cowhig, then respectively publisher and successive editors of *General Practitioner*; Paul Dacre, formerly news editor, now editor at the *Daily Mail*; and Melanie Phillips and Peter Preston, then respectively society editor and editor of *The Guardian*; Chris Horrie, then at the University of Westminster; and James Wilkinson, formerly BBC science correspondent, who recommended me to the University of Cambridge.

I never envisaged becoming a media and presentation skills trainer or a university tutor. I went to the University of Westminster for one day as an external examiner and was invited to teach there. I was subsequently asked to do some media training – another type of teaching. I am indebted to my many media and presentation skills training clients – from CEOs at large companies to small charities and academic institutions.

I also want to thank those who have contributed that most precious of all commodities, their time, to this book by reading and commenting upon it. Their expertise and observations have helped to shape it in so many different ways. They include Professor Susan Bewley, Dr Bob Corringham, Emeritus Professor Ron du Bois, Jenny Bryan, Sir Iain Chalmers, Dr Peter Draper, Professor Harry Dugmore, Professor Marian Fitzgerald, Jenny Hope, Cathy James, Dr Richard Marks, the late Dr Ann McPherson, Nancy Mendoza, David Payne, Dr Columba Quigley, Dr Lisa Schwartz and Gary Schwitzer, Professor Sarah Shepherd, James Wilkinson and Dr Steven Woloshin.

My thanks, too, to journalistic colleagues for giving interviews. They include Rinke van den Brink, Dr Carol Cooper, Dr Oliver Gillie, Anna Larsson, Trudy Lieberman, Dr Ivan Oransky, Charles Ornstein, Gary Schwitzer, Dr Mike Smith and Isabel Walker.

I also wish to gratefully acknowledge the many individuals who have given me permission to reproduce copyright material. They include Annabel Ferriman, Dr Gillie Bolton, Professor Stephen Curry, Dr Ron Daniels, Professor Mark Gabbay, Dr Kate Granger, Melanie Phillips, Andrew Reid, Professor Sarah Shepherd and Professor Lewis Wolpert.

Writing this book has involved meetings with former *Guardian* colleague Bryan McAllister in our "London office", the Wallace Collection, better known as home to one of Europe's finest collections of works of arts, paintings and [oddly] armour and porcelain. I want to say a big thank you to Bryan for his contribution to the cartoons. I was a big McAllister fan long before we met and was delighted when he won a Granada TV *What the Papers Say* Award for his pocket cartoons in *The Guardian*. Unfortunately, he was unable to complete the cartoons for this book. His old friend Ken Pine kindly took over. Thus, unusually there are two cartoon credits: words by Bryan McAllister; drawings by Ken Pine. Ken, many thanks to you too.

Thanks also to my designer, Barry Lowenhoff. Writers often underestimate the importance of designers, forgetting that it is not their words but the design that readers see first. Barry has a deserved reputation for making text accessible and inviting.

Thanks also to Claire Alexander for the cover logo. Claire has a growing reputation as an author and illustrator of children's books. I am glad to have provided another platform for her flair and expertise.

Thanks, too, to my eagle-eyed editor Rose Shepherd for her diligence, flair, enthusiasm and for reining me in when I strayed into the wilderness. The text includes many of her inspired and imaginative ideas.

Finally, thanks to my loving and supportive family: my wife, Liz, and our sons, James and Chris, now two highly accomplished wordsmiths, who have also given me significant help.

Acknowledgments

I also gratefully acknowledge permission to reproduce excerpts from:

Copyright (© 1973) *Medicine and the Mass Media: Answering Press Questions* by M Eastwood and AD Smith. Reproduced by permission of The Royal College of Physicians of Edinburgh.

Copyright (© 1998) Pitfalls of medical journalism by Annabel Ferriman. *HealthWatch Newsletter* No. 28. Reproduced by permission of HealthWatch.

Copyright (© 1973) Structuring and selecting news by J Galtung and MH Ruge, published in *The Manufacture of News: Deviance, Social Problems and the Mass Media,* by Constable, London. Reproduced by permission of the Little, Brown Book Group.

Copyright (© 1997) The Surgery – an insider's view by Mark Gabby. *BMJ* 1997; 314: 1491 http://dx.doi.org/10.1136/bmj.314.7092.1491 Reproduced by permission of the *BMJ*.

Copyright (© 2012) Interview. Edzard Ernst by John Illman *HealthWatch Newsletter* No. 87. Reproduced by permission of HealthWatch.

Copyright (© 2013) *The Social Media HIghway Code* by B Riley and C Gerada. Reproduced by permission of The Royal College of General Practitioners.

Copyright (© 2010) Speak up by Peter Fiske *Nature* 464, 312 (10 March 2010) 10.1038/nj7286-312a Reproduced by permission of *Nature*.

Copyright (© George Orwell 1946) *Politics and The English Language* by George Orwell. Reprinted by permission of Bill Hamilton as the literary executor of the estate of the late Sonia Brownell Orwell.

Copyright (© 1997) The language of medical case histories by W Donnelly. *Annals of Internal Medicine* 127 1045-1048. Reproduced by permission of *The Annals of Internal Medicine*.

Copyright (© 2000) *The Expert Patient* by John Illman. Reproduced by permission of the Association of the British Pharmaceutical Industry.

Copyright (© 2002) Case study workshop. *Guild of Health Writers Newsletter* [Spring]. Reproduced by permission of The Guild of Health Writers.

Copyright (© 2007) Reporting from the edge by Adrian Sudbury. Reproduced by permission of the *Huddersfield Daily Examiner.* Excerpt from *UK Press Gazette:* May 18.

I would also like to acknowledge the following for permission to reproduce graphs, images pictures and slides: emeritus Professor Ron du Bois, Dr Kate Granger, The Burns Archives, Medikidz, shutterstock.com, Science Photo Library.

Introduction

Imagine you are a world authority on the evolution and spread of antibiotic-resistant bacteria. You have just been appointed as department head at a leading European university. A TV science correspondent wants to interview you. You've never been on television before, but you pride yourself on your communication skills. You really do know your subject – you've lectured all over the world.

In the studio you compete for airtime against an earthquake in Chile, a UN world summit, the death of a Hollywood star and arms negotiations in Geneva. You have only three minutes and make every effort to answer the questions and explain the story's complex background. The correspondent isn't interested in your wish to "inform" the audience; she has her own agenda. You spend so much time answering her questions that there is no time for what you want to say. You try to explain; she keeps interrupting.

This is a common experience. Medical researchers are known as poor, often reluctant communicators with the public. Moreover, many clinicians – not without justification – have

reservations about the media. However, if medicine does not represent or communicate its position in the media, it risks being misrepresented.

The words "communication" and "information" are often used interchangeably, but they are not synonymous. Information is about "giving out"; communication is about "getting through". This book is all about getting through. It has been written for healthcare professionals, medical researchers, press officers, PR practitioners and people working for medical charities. It includes:

Chapter One *Journalists*. Who are the reporters behind the headlines and what drives them? Their stories are rarely told. Knowing how they think and work should make you a better communicator.

Chapter Two *The news business*. What makes news? Healthcare professionals frequently tell journalists: "You should write about this." They may be right, but the worthy and the newsworthy are not necessarily the same. Knowing what makes news is a prerequisite for effective communication in the media.

Chapter Three *Responding to a media interview request* highlights common errors. Inappropriate responses to interview requests are probably the most common reason for bad outcomes.

Chapter Four *Preparing for a media interview* is about defining objectives, developing messages and anticipating and answering questions. Preparation is essential when an ill-advised comment can go around the world in seconds.

Chapter Five *Different types of interview* describes how to respond when the interviewer and interviewee have the same agenda and – critically – when they don't.

Chapter Six *Making an impression* covers the varying demands of different interview formats such as recorded and live broadcast interviews, and examines issues such as press conferences and your right to see an article featuring or mentioning you, before publication.

Chapter Seven *Writing for the media* is about finding your voice, developing and submitting ideas, research, interviewing, the writing process and the different storytelling traditions in medicine and the media.

Chapter Eight *Social media and blogging* explains how blogging has shaken up and extended medical writing, and the importance of Twitter in establishing a digital identity. It warns about the risks of presenting yourself to the online world without training and without the restraining hands of an editor and protection of peer review.

Chapter Nine *Presenting to the media and other audiences* is about planning and giving a talk that may become headline news.

Chapter Ten *Patient case histories – a suitable case for treatment* examines the benefits and risks for patients who speak to journalists. It points out that media interviewees are often the very opposite of what you may expect – impulsive and over-trusting rather than cagey and cautious.

Chapter Eleven *Narrative medicine – keep taking the words* explores how writers such as the twice winner of the Man Booker Prize Hilary Mantel and the late British journalist John Diamond have used writing to manage and understand their illnesses and to reach out to fellow patients. This chapter also looks at the role of therapeutic writing for healthcare professionals.

Chapter Twelve *Medicine and the media: 1950-2000. A brief history* looks at key developments that have shaped medical and health journalism since World War Two. These include the thalidomide tragedy, consumerism, the first human-to-human heart transplant and the internet.

Chapter 1
Journalists

Read this chapter to find out about:

COMMON LINKS BETWEEN JOURNALISTS AND HEALTHCARE PROFESSIONALS

DIFFERENT TYPES OF JOURNALISTS

THE NATURE OF JOURNALISM

WHAT MAKES A MEDICAL JOURNALIST

THE MEDICINE-MEDIA RELATIONSHIP

Medicine and the media may have disparate standards, but healthcare professionals and journalists have much in common. In good interviews/consultations skilled clinicians/journalists:

- Are curious
- Take good notes
- Are not judgemental
- Put interviewees/patients at ease
- Actively encourage interviewees/patients to talk
- Show understanding and empathy.
- Ask clear questions
- Ask open questions that cannot be answered with "yes" or "no"
- Ask closed questions requiring a "yes" or "no" to obtain and classify simple facts
- Listen with genuine interest [to what is and isn't being said]
- Gather a lot of relevant information quickly
- Watch for giveaway facial expressions.

A report published by the Royal College of Physicians of Edinburgh noted: "Doctors and journalists belong to professions which have intimate contact with the public." From here the gulf widens. "Doctors are constrained to further the public good by considering the wellbeing of the individual. Journalists, conversely, often use the individual to increase public interest, which, when aroused, can improve the fortunes of the individual or the community. The doctor is aware that when the excitement of the crisis is over, he will continue to see his patient or the surviving family. In contrast, the interest of the press in the individual wanes after the crisis, except when a follow-up article, months later, may serve to revive that interest temporarily. The journalist moves on to write for his public."[1]

Public esteem

Healthcare professionals are generally held in high public esteem: people want to believe the very best of those who may determine whether they live or die. Journalists are not so well regarded. For example, in a US public opinion poll based on ten occupational groups, published in 2013 by the Pew Forum on Religion and Public Life, only 28 per cent of respondents agreed that journalists "contribute a lot to society". Only business executives and lawyers ranked lower. Medical doctors [66 per cent] were

"Our first daughter is a journalist. The second is an estate agent and our son is a banker - where did we go wrong?"

among the most well regarded, below the military [78 per cent] and teachers [72 per cent].[2]

Journalists, unlike doctors, are their own worst public relations officers.[3] They tend to be outsiders. As the British media pundit Roy Greenslade observed, journalism, by its nature, is anti-establishment, intrusive, challenging and confrontational.[4] It should dig deep below the surface to expose the grime below. It can be a shady business involving deceit and guile. The late British journalist Nicholas Tomalin wrote in 1969 that the only essential attributes for journalistic success were ratlike cunning, a plausible manner, and a little literary ability.[5] Yet we often have good reason to be grateful to journalists.

What do journalists do?
As a media interviewee you may speak to a:
- General reporter
- Specialist correspondent
- Feature writer
- TV or radio researcher

These may be either staff, or freelances who may work for many different outlets. Freelances sell either news or feature articles or broadcast material. Many clinicians are similarly part-time freelances.

General reporters are assigned stories by the news editor. They may handle specialist medical or scientific stories if a specialist is unavailable, or if the news team lacks a dedicated medical specialist.

Specialist medical or scientific correspondents produce their own news and feature ideas, feeding them through the news/features editor. Most medical correspondents are not medically qualified.

Feature writers present the background to the news or people in the news. Written by specialists and non-specialists, feature articles tend to be longer than news stories, typically 600 to 2,000 words.

Researchers prepare storylines and find potential interviewees for feature writers or reporters or producers.

What makes a specialist medical journalist?

I edited a specialist journal [*New Psychiatry*] and a medical newspaper [*GP*] and worked as a national newspaper medical correspondent and health editor. This made me a journalistic "specialist". But I was, in essence, a generalist. How could I be otherwise if, say, I worked with cardiologists on Monday, immunologists on Tuesday, geriatricians on Wednesday, a patient group on Thursday and politicians on Friday?

What made me a specialist was my contacts book, a broad familiarity with developments across the healthcare spectrum, the ability to "spot" a story and "sell" it to the news or features editor, and good social skills. The latter are critical in cultivating contacts. My contacts book includes, for example, email addresses and office, cell/mobile and home telephone numbers of about 30 cardiologists. Ready access to expert opinion is a prerequisite for a specialist. Contacts are more important than medical knowledge, which may be out of date. No individual can keep up to date with the mass of healthcare developments.

Surely, though, the more specialist knowledge a "specialist" journalist has, the better? This isn't actually a clear-cut issue. Understanding biostatistics and epidemiology, and knowing about specific disease areas clearly makes it easier to frame critical questions, but specialist knowledge may isolate a specialist reporter from his or her core audience. I started in journalism as a drama critic after working in the theatre. What I wrote as a drama critic, I now recognise, was directed more at the people on the stage than my readers. [In mitigation, I was a very young drama critic!] Specialist reporters can also become too close to their contacts.

An opposing view by Dr Ragnar Levi in his exceptional book on medical journalism is that specialist knowledge in a fast-moving, complex field such as medicine outweighs the potential drawbacks.[6] He has a point but, as US journalist Gary Schwitzer explains later in this chapter, a good reporter compensates for limits in expertise. A good reporter will also recognise that the hardest thing of all to do in journalism is to tell the truth. It is akin to a greyhound chasing an electric hare. No matter how hard you run, it is, more often than not, just not fast enough. Just as the hare is tantalisingly out of reach, so is the truth. Reporting what you are told – the easy part – may not be good enough.

Facts don't speak for themselves, as some people would have us believe. They contradict one another. They need to be interpreted and spoken for, and they shift and change according to who is interpreting them. The late Enoch Powell, a former UK government health secretary and one of the most controversial British politicians of the 20th century, told me: "When the geriatricians tell me they need more money, I take no notice. When the geriatricians tell me the paediatricians need more money, I am all ears." Good journalists, like Powell, do not accept what they are told at face value.

Who are medical journalists?
Young people do not yearn to be medical journalists as they aspire to be football stars or astronauts. Medical journalism is almost always an accidental career. For example, I went for an interview for a job on an engineering magazine. It had gone, but *GP* newspaper, located next door, wanted freelances. Twenty minutes later I had a commission to write a profile about the then Amateur Boxing Association medical officer, Dr Joseph Lewis Blonstein. More than 30 years later, I am still writing about medicine and healthcare.

As Annabel Ferriman, the *BMJ's* senior news editor and a former UK national newspaper correspondent, explained: "Newspapers are not universities. They don't pay journalists to research into medical matters, fully inform them then occasionally impart some wisdom. One day a journalist is a general reporter, the next... a medical correspondent."[7]

Formerly CNN's medical correspondent, Gary Schwitzer publishes the US *Health News Review*, which aims to improve the accuracy of news stories about medical treatments, tests, products and procedures, and to help consumers to evaluate the evidence for and against new ideas in health care. Using a standardised rating system, a multi-disciplinary team of reviewers assess the quality of media medical stories and publish the results.

Now adjunct associate professor in the University of Minnesota School of Public Health, Schwitzer initially wanted to be a sports reporter. Although he had been an "A" student, he was not especially interested in science. He explained: "I left college for a TV station where there were already lots of veteran sports journalists, and so I was biding my time. I was editing tapes and writing and editing scripts, but I wasn't on air. One day the news director tapped me on the shoulder and said: 'Kid, we figure you want to be on air. Here's your chance. We're going to start a medical news beat. It's yours if you want it – because no one else wants it. No one wants to deal with doctors full time.' "

Why? "Doctors were viewed as a pain in the ass. Cumbersome. They required you to decipher their complex language and I think it is fair to say that medicine wasn't viewed – and it sometimes still isn't – as a meaty beat. It was seen as fluffy – the biggest baby in town was born today... the ribbon-cutting ceremony at the opening of a new hospital wing... that sort of thing. Fast forward to today and you see tremendous changes, but there is a spectrum from Pulitzer Prizes to putrid, and, unfortunately, putrid wins out on many days.

"So I fell into the job for all the wrong reasons. This still happens today." Like many medical journalists, Schwitzer did not have statistical training. He says: "One of my strengths is to admit my weaknesses, and despite how we might come across as being expert, I admit I still struggle. This should not be an embarrassment or a hindrance. Knowing what you don't know, but quickly, on the heels of that, knowing where to go to get help, is smart."

Rinke van den Brink, health editor for NOS News, the Dutch public broadcasting service, had no formal journalistic training, but served a long apprenticeship – beginning when he was just ten years old. Writing his own newspaper by hand, he sold it in his street for the equivalent of a few pence or cents. He later began submitting freelance articles to a newspaper that eventually gave him a full-time job on the foreign desk. He spent about 25 years working in newspapers, radio and TV before specialising in health. The author of five books, four about the extreme right in Europe and one about antimicrobial resistance, he enjoys the complexity and variety of health reporting and the opportunity to produce one-to two-minute pieces for TV, four-to five-minute pieces for radio and longer written pieces for the internet, typically 500 words. One-or two-minute reports may sound superficial, but he says: "It's surprising how much you can say in a minute or two."[9] This is an important message for all media interviewees.

Anna Larsson spent the first three years of her career as a local newspaper reporter before deciding to do something "more substantial". After three years as a medical student she recognised that she was "a writing person" and didn't want to be a doctor. She went on to work in radio in her native Sweden more than 20 years ago and explained: "I hear something new every day, and compared to my colleagues, I think that I get a bigger response because what I do is close to the heart of the audience – everything from insect bites to transplants."[10]

Dr Ivan Oransky is the only person I know who had teenage ambitions to go into medical journalism. Formerly executive editor of *Reuter's Health* in New York and then global editorial director of medpagetoday.com, he left clinical practice for full-time medical journalism. He recalled: "When I was in college I was very active with my daily college newspaper. I was executive editor. I had the same training by the time I left college that many people in journalism have.

"I continued to do journalism in medical school, but not mainstream journalism. I was co-editor-in-chief of the medical students' section of *JAMA* [The Journal of the American Medical Association]. I did a lot of op eds[11] and some reporting. When I was an intern I had a couple of newspaper columns, and I realised I was having far more fun doing that – and so decided to do it full time."[12]

Many doctors combine clinical and media work. Dr Carol Cooper finds writing and TV a welcome counterpoint to the treadmill of general practice. As *The Sun* doctor, a regular TV contributor and a prolific author, she is one of Britain's high-profile media medics. At the time of writing, the bright and breezy *Sun*, one of the world's top-selling newspapers, has a circulation well over two million.

Cooper began studying physics at Cambridge before switching to medicine. Her journalism career began with lighthearted contributions to *Hospital Doctor* and the *BMJ* that, she now says, "were not very good". Being a funny writer is notoriously hard, but Cooper became a regular contributor to Britain's foremost humour magazine, *Punch*.

Has her media career made her a better doctor? "I think writing for *The Sun* has, because it forces me to be concise and clear and to use simple words to communicate complex ideas. The same is true of TV. It's an extension of my writing, expressing complex ideas in simple words – and not very many of them. I like the immediacy of TV. You have to get it right or nearly right first time. But when it's done, it's done."[13]

Isabel Walker's interest in journalism began at university in the UK. She went on to edit *Medeconomics* and to be medical correspondent on the *Daily Mail* and the *Sunday Telegraph*. She recalled: "I had wanted to be an actress, but gradually I realised that I was no more than a competent performer. After I'd written for the university magazine the editor suggested I should become a journalist. My boyfriend at the time was a medical student. After he'd qualified and we'd married, I moved from a weekly to an evening newspaper where I was given the medical stories because it was assumed I had the right contacts.

"My then husband was president of the British Medical Students' Association. He invited the famous medical journalist and broadcaster Dr Michael O'Donnell, editor of *World Medicine*, to be a dinner guest speaker. Sitting next to Michael I moaned about how awful it was to be married to a junior doctor. He asked me to write an article about it. When I moved to

London, he encouraged me to become a medical journalist. I'd no idea that the speciality existed, but I got a job on *GP*. It helped that my husband was about to train as a GP."[14]

Charles Ornstein is a senior reporter at ProPublica, an independent, non-profit, New York newsroom that produces "investigative journalism in the public interest". He recalled: "I didn't go to journalism school, but I was the editor of my college and high school papers. I began my career with the *Dallas Morning News* covering two suburbs. I'd been doing this for about a year when I was given the option either to cover the police for the main metro desk or healthcare for the business desk.

"As I was considering what to do, a mentor asked: 'What do you want to do when you grow up?' I said I'd really like to be a reporter in Washington, DC. He advised me to take the healthcare beat because metro and police reporters were a dime a dozen. I quickly discovered healthcare journalism was more than just a job. It was a passion. So it was something I stumbled into – luckily."[15]

Why do so many medical journalists, like Ornstein, feel passionate about what they do? I believe it is because medical and health journalism focuses on fundamental life-and-death issues, right and wrong, safety and survival, hope and fear, risk and benefit, cutting-edge technology, the bedside manner, the life cycle, money, the politics of health, doctor-patient communication, self help, living with chronic disease, abortion, family planning, animal research plus much more.

The medicine-media relationship
Despite allegations that the media demonise medicine and bay for its blood, almost all contacts between healthcare professionals and journalists are amicable. I know this from more than 30 years of reporting. The media are not generally out to get healthcare professionals, although there are times when they should do and do; times when they should but don't; and times when they shouldn't but do.

Some lapses, probably most, arise from honest mistakes; some from poor communication; and some, lamentably, from reckless spin and distortion. But journalists – as we will see later – are as much spinned against as spinners themselves. This brings me to a pivotal issue. "Balance", the direct opposite of spinning, is recognised as the hallmark of good journalism, a fair way of telling both sides of a story, a means of being objective and preventing bias. Balance can work well in straightforward stories: a government minister and their shadow can be given equal time or space to state opposing views; a residents' association can speak out against a radical council plan. But balanced medical and science stories can distort research and provoke pseudo controversy.

Remarkably, journalistic "balance" is rarely discussed in public forums – and when it is, it is not because of scientific considerations. For example, in July 2015, British Cabinet ministers were widely reported as insisting that the BBC "can't be impartial" about terrorists. Chris Grayling, leader of the House of Commons, insisted that the broadcaster should not seek to be any more balanced towards Isis [the extremist group Islamic State] than it was towards the Nazis.

This raises an intriguing question. Which stories/topics merit balance and which do not? Dr Edzard Ernst, formerly Britain's first professor of complementary medicine at the University of Exeter, says: "Imagine that *National Geographic* were to publish an article 'balancing' existing scientific knowledge by presenting the opinions of the Flat Earth Society. Who would take it seriously? Yet we regularly accept the equivalent when discussing homeopathy."

His point was that the scientific evidence for homeopathy is as robust as that stating the world is flat. There is no scientific rationale for assuming that homoeopathic remedies – which are devoid of pharmacologically active molecules – can produce clinical effects. Any benefits must be restricted to placebo. Yet if I were writing a piece about the science of homeopathy, convention would demand that I balance the story with comment from a homeopath. A practitioner would probably steadfastly insist that science didn't know everything and that he had hundreds if not thousands of satisfied patients.

Concessions to balance sometimes mean that lone mavericks may be given as much time or space as heavily peer-reviewed researchers who represent international scientific consensus. This can create a misleading idea that there is an ongoing scientific debate between two hypotheses of equal weight. In the case of homoeopathy, there is no debate to be had. The same is true, in one sense, of tobacco. The tobacco industry has always insisted that in the interests of balance, it has a right to be heard. This has given it a priceless platform to defend itself against overwhelming scientific evidence that it has contributed to the premature deaths of millions of people, thus perpetuating a debate that should have ended decades ago.

I first questioned traditional notions about balance while writing a piece for *The Sunday Times* about a man who had set himself up as a "psychotherapist" after running a marriage bureau and social club. He was completely untrained, but within the law. Anyone in Britain could and still can call themselves a psychotherapist despite evidence that unqualified practitioners can do significant harm. His clients included people suffering from stress, tension, depression and even sexual problems.

Yet the "story" had to be balanced. I quoted him as saying that the mistake many psychiatrists made was that they "treated the field as 100 per cent science" when you needed "an intuitive feeling". He added: "No exams, no degrees can show if you've got that or not." The story was further "balanced" by legal advice that we should describe him as "a reputable therapist" to eliminate any libel risk. A few days later he called to thank me. He said that he had been inundated by calls from new clients who had read about him in *The Sunday Times*. Balance had demolished my hatchet job.

Of course the right kind of journalistic balance is essential. The late American astronomer and author Carl Sagan called upon science journalists to balance their genuine sense of wonder about new developments with old-fashioned scepticism. This need is as great as ever. In 1994, Professor Doug Altman, one of the world's leading medical statisticians, estimated that only one per cent of medical research was free from flaws.[16] In 2009 Sir Iain Chalmers, an internationally acclaimed Oxford-based researcher, and his Australian colleague Professor Paul Glasziou, estimated that as much as 85 per cent of research investment was wasted.[17] In 2014 a supplement in *The Lancet* medical journal raised similar concerns.[18]

This underlines the need for reputable healthcare professionals and scientists to work with the media. But there is often an imbalance between people who should be speaking to the media and those who should not. Many of those who should not speak but do, score over scientists who should speak but don't because of a naive belief that "the evidence will speak for itself". Vociferous lobbies and snake-oil salesmen appreciate the importance of engaging with the media more readily than reputable, ethical experts who stand back in fear that reporters may misquote them or dumb down their work. This is a risk, but almost all reporters want to get things right. They are only as good as their sources. Sources who understand how the news business works are better able to work with the media. I hope that the next chapter – which is all about news values, the raw ingredients of news – will promote such understanding.

SUMMARY

- Medicine and the media may have disparate standards, but healthcare professionals and journalists have much in common.
- Journalism can be a dirty, irresponsible business employing deceit and guile, but the world often has good reason to be grateful to journalists.
- Contacts and access to up-to-date information are more important to journalists than knowledge [that may be out of date].
- A part-time journalistic career can be a welcome counterpoint to the treadmill of clinical practice.
- Journalists are themselves as much spinned against as spinners.

NOTES AND REFERENCES

1 Eastwood M, Smith AD (1973) *Medicine and the Mass Media: Answering Press Questions* p 6 Royal College of Physicians of Edinburgh

2 http://www.salon.com/2013/07/13/poll_journalists_only_slightly_more_respected_than_lawyers_partner/

3 Observation by the late Tony Thistlethwaite, former press officer, British Medical Association; author, *Independent and Bloody Minded: The Story of the Medical Journalists' Association* 1967-97

4 Greenslade R (2005) Nobody likes us, we don't care *The Guardian* Jan 17

5 Tomalin N (1969) *The Sunday Times Magazine.* October 26.

6 Levi R (2001) *Medical Journalism: Exposing Fact, Fiction, Fraud* pp 5-6 Wiley

7 Ferriman A (1998) Pitfalls of medical journalism *HealthWatch* newsletter no 28

8 Schwitzer G (2011) Interview with JI. University of Coventry, UK. European conference on health journalism, Health in the Headlines.

9 van den Brink R (2014) Interview with JI. University of Coventry, UK, during the 2nd international conference on health journalism, First Do No Harm

10 Larsson A (2011) Interview with JI. University of Coventry. As ref. 8

11 An op ed article expresses the views of the writer. The term is an abbreviation for "opposite the editorial page". Op eds are often mistaken for editorials, which are usually anonymous.

12 Oransky I (2011) Interview with JI. University of Coventry, UK. As ref. 8

13 Cooper C (2015) Interview with JI

14 Walker I (2011) Interview with JI during medical journalism seminar, University of Westminster.

15 Ornstein C (2011) Interview with JI. University of Coventry, UK. As ref. 8

16 Altman DG (1994) The scandal of poor medical research *BMJ* 308: 283-284

17 Chalmers I, Glasziou P (2009) Avoidable waste in the production and reporting of research evidence *The Lancet* 374: 86-89

18 Chalmers I et al (2014) Research: increasing value, reducing waste. Supplement. *The Lancet* January 18.

Chapter 2

The news business. What makes news?

Read this chapter to find out about:

CONSTITUENTS OF NEWS

NEWS VALUES

THE NEWS AGENDA

HOW SCIENTISTS CAN BE WOEFULLY UNSCIENTIFIC

Healthcare professionals frequently say to journalists: "You should write about this, it's important." They are usually right, but there is a critical difference between the worthy and the newsworthy. No news means no story. "Smoking is life threatening", for example, is an important message, but it is no longer news. It was news in 1950 when Richard Doll and Austin Bradford Hill highlighted the link between smoking and lung cancer.[1]

I once failed to distinguish between the worthy and the newsworthy. Wanting to write about bowel cancer, I pitched an idea to Paul Dacre, then the London *Daily Mail* news editor, later editor. He exploded: "Who the hell wants to read about bowel cancer over breakfast?" In fact, it wasn't readership sensitivity to bowels over breakfast that was the real problem so much as the story idea. It wasn't news. Three weeks later everything changed when US President Ronald Reagan was reported to have had bowel cancer surgery.[2] The next day people all over the world read and heard about bowel cancer over breakfast. Reagan was one of the most famous of men, in one of the most demanding of jobs. [See note 2 for information on the public's right to know about the health of the President.]

News takes many different forms and is almost always a reaction to change. If I had to choose just one word to sum up news it would be "change". There are exceptions to this rule. For example, the then London *Sunday Times* editor Harold ["Harry"] Evans [now Sir Harold] wanted a news story about paranoia. No one knew why. Paranoia had not been debated by MPs or been the subject of a major investigation. I was instructed to write this "editor's must". Within three hours I produced a story that started:

Doctors are worried about the increasing number of "amateur psychiatrists" and others who are misusing the medical term of paranoia. Because it is being used liberally in a colloquial sense, it often creates difficulties for people with genuine grievances.[3]

Newspapers and radio and TV stations followed it up and, to my great surprise, MPs did then debate it. It *became* news.

What is news?

News can be anything that makes the audience say "gee whiz!" or "fancy that!" or makes them think: "That could be me!" The British medical writer Dr Michael O'Donnell identified three types of medical news: the major breakthrough, the major scare and the major scandal. A *Psychiatric Bulletin* editorial[4] suggested that there are four basic types of health story: the scare story [eg, "flesh-eating bug"]; the cure story [eg, "magic bullet drug breakthrough"]; the money story [eg, "hospital fails after cash cuts"] and the human-interest story [eg, "My struggle with bulimia"].

But a story can be a story if a reporter thinks it is. For example, Munchausen syndrome fascinates me. I have written Munchausen stories that other specialist writers would ignore because I am amazed that people go to such extraordinary lengths to feign illness in themselves or, even more alarming, in their children ["by proxy"]. What editors think is even more important than what reporters think. The *Daily Mail* once sent me to Canada and the US to report on the hair-restoring power of the antihypertensive agent minoxidil. I suspect my trip was linked to the small bald patch on the head of the then editor, the late Sir David English, and his recognition that the quest to grow hair on balding male heads was as old as time and would appeal to millions of readers.

English had extraordinary "news sense" – the ability to "see" or "taste" a story. Journalists describe this as a gut instinct or a "nose for news". Some people have it, others don't. I have it. Many people far cleverer than me don't. Good news sense can help a reporter to spot a 500-word story in a 10,000-word report or to pick up a winning, throwaway line in a presentation. For example, a scientist was talking about the technology of devising metals that retain their shape when warm. It was all mundane stuff until he suggested, in a "fancy that!" moment, that the technology could be used to fashion a bra that would remember a woman's exact shape.[5]

News: good and bad

"New" is a seductive word. Think how we react to the idea of a new house, a new start, a new car, a new relationship. In recent times more than 90 UK media titles have included the word "new" – from *New Direction* to *New Start* to *New Woman*.[6] But while "new" is generally synonymous with hope, "news" is often associated with misery and adversity. Beverley Parkin, in her former role as director of public affairs at the Royal Pharmaceutical Society, insisted: "Good news is no news as far as the media are concerned."[7] Another view is that: "There is no such thing as good or bad news, there is only news."[8]

Just to confuse things even more, in another sense, "bad news" could be said to be "good news". A report that premature babies were 48 times more likely to die from cot death if they were placed to sleep on their fronts instead of their backs reflected tragedy but had life-saving potential. A *BMJ* study classified 89 healthcare stories in two UK newspapers, *The Times* and *The Sun*, as either "good news", "bad news" or "neutral".[9] The articles were based on papers in *The Lancet* and the *BMJ* in 1999 and 2000. For example, an association between jogging and a beneficial effect on mortality was "good news"; a finding that infants who slept with their parents on a sofa were at increased risk of sudden death was "bad news"; and a report that severe life events around conception reduced the proportion of male babies was "neutral". Again, the "bad news" example had life-saving potential. Classifying news as "good" or "bad" can be simplistic and unscientific.

News values
The raw constituents of news, news values include:
- Novelty
- Universality
- Topicality
- Impact
- Controversy

Novelty
Superlatives underline novelty appeal. For example:
- first
- best
- biggest
- smallest

'Firsts' produce powerful stories. The first successful human-to-human kidney transplant [1954]; the first human-to-human liver transplant [1963]; the first human- to- human heart transplant [1967]; the first human full face transplant [2010]... This emphasis on 'firsts' may seem restrictive. There can only be one first-operation-of-its kind story, but try tapping "transplant news" into Google – journalistic novelty has many faces. A simple way to evaluate a story's novelty appeal and newsworthiness is to ask if the first paragraph will tell the audience something that is new and meaningful to them – it doesn't have to be literally "new".

Universality

The more common and threatening an illness, the greater its news potential: thus heart disease and cancer produce more stories than psoriasis and eczema. A psoriasis story may be novel, but appeal only to a minority. There is an exception to this rule below.

Topicality

Daily news is about yesterday, today and tomorrow, not three months ago, or three months hence. Conversely, by virtue of topicality, a story theme with no news value today can be tomorrow's front page headline. The US President Ronald Reagan bowel cancer story was a classic example, while the internationally acclaimed Dennis Potter TV drama series *The Singing Detective* generated extensive coverage about psoriasis. TV soap opera medical story lines also reach huge audiences, many of them young viewers who wouldn't normally sit down and watch a news programme or documentary about, say, breast cancer or depression.

Topical stories are either "diary stories" or "off-the-diary stories". Also known as "breaking news" or "hard news", off-the-diary stories feature the unexpected such as a train crash or a hurricane. Diary stories may be known about months or even years in advance, allowing for long-term planning for seasonal topics such as SAD [Seasonal affective disorder] and flu.

Impact

This may be emotional or dramatic. An anniversary story I wrote for *The Guardian*[10] had strong emotional and scientific appeal. It started: *"Britain's first heart transplant was carried out 25 years ago today on a 45-year-old man from Leigh-on-Sea in Essex. Fred West had already undergone 20 operations and was critically ill. The operation at the National Heart Hospital was proclaimed 'a success' and the transplant team waved Union Jacks as medicine… went public as never before. The euphoria was tempered by theologians, lawyers, philosophers; by a Guardian editorial declaring 'we are*

*all potential donors now'; and finally, 46 days later, by West's death. West was,
in effect, as much a donor as recipient. The justification for surgery was that
without a transplant he would have died anyway."*

No other organ has so much emotional appeal as the heart. There are heroic
hearts, stout ones, kind ones, pure ones, hearts of oak, hearts of stone,
hearts of gold. Generations of poets and writers have set apart the heart,
which has no power over feeling, for this special treatment in preference to
the brain, the source of all thoughts and actions.

Logically, the brain would be a better choice, but logic does not lend itself
to romance, and the brain does not easily lend itself to symbolism. The
heart's shape is more attractive than that of the brain's — it is not unlike the
Valentine emblem. More critically, we can feel our hearts responding to the
thrill of love or fear. We never feel the brain.

An emotional soundbite can lift a story that may otherwise be an also ran.
The late children's author Roald Dahl hit the headlines when he declared:
"It really is almost a crime to allow your child to go unimmunised."[11] His
eldest daughter, Olivia, had died from measles encephalitis at the age of
seven before a vaccine became available. No one knew better than Dahl
about the power of the soundbite.

Controversy

Many healthcare professionals avoid the media for fear of controversy, but
controversy can drive change and *usually* presents more of an opportunity
than a threat for media interviewees. Sidestepping a media interview may
mean that your voice will be unheard, perhaps leaving an open platform for
scaremongers and mavericks.

Again, vaccination is a case in point. Following a press conference in
1998 at the Royal Free Hospital, London, in which the now discredited Dr
Andrew Wakefield expressed concern about the safety of the MMR vaccine,
MMR coverage in the UK fell from 88 per cent in 1998-1989 to 80 per
cent in 2003-2004. This was an example of the power of lobbying. Few
lobbies have been more vociferous than the anti-vaccine lobby. The MMR
controversy highlighted the need for journalistic balance in health and
science reporting. Balance is discussed in Chapter One: *Journalists.*

News values

Value	Marks (out of 10)
Novelty	
Universality	
Topicality	
Impact	
Controversy	

Use this scale to evaluate a story's newsworthiness, allocating a maximum ten points to each value. Only exceptional stories score the maximum 50 points. For example, the first test-tube baby (1978); Dolly the Sheep, the first ovine superstar (1996); the first penis transplant (2015). Any story scoring more than 15 on the scale may attract publicity on a "typical" news day. But no story is an island (see below).

The news agenda: no story is an island

Individual news stories are part of a news agenda comprising hundreds of different stories, everything from health and politics to education and sport. The daily news agenda may be either broad, allowing for a large number of wide-ranging stories, or narrow, resulting in a small range, led by a big "parent story". The 9/11 terrorist outrage was a spectacular example of the latter

On the night of November 18, 1987, I was writing the *Daily Mail* front page "splash" about the Royal College of Nursing [RCN] when we first heard about a fire at the King's Cross Tube [subway] station in London, in which 31 people were to die and 100 more were injured. My RCN story finally made three paragraphs on about page 50. Major off-the-diary stories can displace important health stories altogether. Conversely, a lesser health story may lead the news on a so-called "slow" news day. Yes – news is a lottery. A strong story may also be rejected for balance. No one wants 20 bank robbery stories or 20 medical stories on the same day.

Thus a medical correspondent may be asked for a lighter story on a gloomy news day to achieve a different kind of journalistic balance to that discussed in Chapter One: *Journalists* on pages 24-25.

Johan Galtung and Mari Ruge identified other factors affecting news selection:[12]

Short time span: events that unfold and acquire meaning quickly and that fit into the media's daily production routine are preferable to long-term processes.

For example, a new operation or a drug launch.

Scale and intensity: any event must pass a certain threshold before it is recorded at all. An issue perceived as more significant than others is obviously more likely to be reported: this perception is influenced by previous media coverage.

For example, HIV/AIDS initially attracted little media attention. As happens so often in the history of medicine, early cases were considered isolated extremes in the spectrum of normal illness.[13]

The first pictures of Francis Crick and James Watson with their original model of the DNA double helix in Cambridge in 1953 is perhaps the most spectacular example of the media initially ignoring a significant development. *Time* magazine returned the negatives to the highly acclaimed photographer, Antony Barrington Brown. The editors did not realise that the pictures were the first of one of the century's greatest scientific stories. They were not alone. Astonishingly, as *The Times* of London noted in 2012, the pictures remained unpublished for at least ten years.[14] The late Barrington Brown and his estate eventually made more money from one of them than from all the rest of his pictures put together.[15]

Photo credit: *A. Barrington Brown, Gonville and Caius College/ Science Photo Library*

Clarity: clear and unequivocal issues are more likely to be covered than those that are ambiguous or less obviously good or bad.

Journalists and consumers want certainty. Medical science doesn't do certainty. Sir Kenneth Calman, then chief medical officer at the Department of Health in London, pointed out that the uncertainty in science sometimes made it hard to present the public with clear information. People, he said, were entitled to as much information as possible, but they had to recognise that any available information may be incomplete."[16]

Meaningfulness: cultural proximity and relevance are the criteria that rule here. The familiar and culturally similar will get particular attention.

Consonance: the media prefer stories that reinforce society's existing expectations.

Paradoxically, news editors may shy away from stories that break new ground. In evaluating scores of stories they make snap judgements, often within seconds, as to whether or not to use them. This is easier if decision-making involves familiar topics or themes. Medical and health correspondents [who propose story ideas to news editors] commonly complain that "the news desk can't 'see' a good exclusive". Ultimately such a story may become someone else's exclusive. There are few things more galling than being asked to follow up what should have been your exclusive. Point out to the news desk that you had it first and the classic response is: "Well, it shouldn't take you long to write, should it?"

Unexpectedness: unusual and surprising events have the highest chance of becoming news.

This – as the previous comment illustrates – is true only up to a point. Some stories "break" or emerge before their time. The pivotal study by Richard Doll and Austin Bradford Hill, in 1950, linking smoking and lung cancer, was largely ignored initially because smoking was regarded as normal and harmless.[17] Doll and Hill had thought it would probably identify pollution from coal fires, tarring of the roads, and exhaust fumes as the most likely causes of lung cancer.[18] Their findings, though correct, sounded implausible at the time and led to widespread public denial.

Continuity: once something has made the headlines, it will continue to be defined as news for some time, even if coverage falls significantly.

Again HIV/AIDS is a classic example.

Understanding the news business is a critical prerequisite for deciding whether or not to accept a media interview request. This topic is explored in the next two chapters.

SUMMARY

- It is critical to distinguish the newsworthy from the worthy
- News is determined by "news values" such as novelty, topicality, universality, impact and controversy
- No story is an island. The daily news agenda can be either very broad, allowing for a wide range of stories, or very narrow, producing a limited range. An international crisis such as 9/11 creates a very narrow focus: a single major story may command 70 per cent of total news coverage. This may exclude important health stories
- A news event must pass a certain threshold before it is recorded as news. For example, HIV/AIDS initially attracted little attention.

NOTES AND REFERENCES

1   Doll R, Hill AB (1950). Smoking and Carcinoma of the Lung; preliminary report *BMJ* 2:739 http://www.ncbi.nlm.nih.gov/pmc/articles/PMC2557577/

2   Reagan was reported to have undergone surgery in 1985. The public's right to know about the health of the President had become a talking point. For example, John F Kennedy's Addison's disease was purposely obfuscated before his election. See Annas GJ (1995) The health of the President and Presidential candidates – the public's right to know *New England Journal of Medicine* 333 945-949. The question of celebrities and patient confidentiality is discussed further in Chapter Eleven: *Media case histories: a suitable case for treatment.*

3   I have the cutting of this story: the date has been detached.

4   Salter M, Byrne P (2000) The stigma of mental illness: how you can use the media to reduce it *Psychiatric Bulletin* 24 281-283

5   White S, Evans P, Mihill C Tysoe M (1993) *Hitting The Headlines* pp18-19 BPS Books

6   *Willings Press Guide* (2002) UK Periodicals Classified Index

7   Parkin B (1992) Media matters. *Pharmaceutical Journal* January 25. pp 122-123

8   Clayton J, Street J (1998) *Health and the Media* p 8. Association of Healthcare Communicators

9   Bartlett C, Sterne J, Egger M (2002) What is newsworthy? Longitudinal study of the reporting of medical research *BMJ* 325 81-84

10   Illman J (1993) A tale to break your new heart *G2* cover story. *The Guardian* May 4

11   Illman J (1988) It's almost a crime not to vaccinate, says Dahl *Daily Mail* March 17

12   Galtung J, Ruge MH (1973) Structuring and selecting news. In Cohen S, Young J (eds) The *Manufacture of News: Deviance, Social Problems and the Mass Media* Constable, London.Galtung J, Ruge MH (1965) The structure of foreign news 2 641-91

13   Cahill KM (1984) *The AIDS Epidemic* p 1 Hutchinson, London

14   *The Times* (2012) Antony Barrington Brown (obituary) February 13. P 52

15   Ibid

16   Calman K (1996) Science and society and the communication of risk *BMJ* 313 799-802

17   Doll R, Hill AB (1950). Smoking and Carcinoma of the Lung; preliminary report *BMJ* 2:739 http://www.ncbi.nlm.nih.gov/pmc/articles/PMC2557577/

18   Ibid

Chapter 3

Responding to a media interview request

Read this chapter to find out about:

HOW TO AVOID POSSIBLE DISASTER

WHETHER OR NOT TO GRANT AN INTERVIEW REQUEST

DIFFERENT INTERVIEW SCENARIOS

In the 1980s I was a young researcher on a BBC TV *Panorama* inquiry
into a controversial anti-arthritic medicine that had been withdrawn
from sale.[1] The reporter, Tom Mangold, not a medical expert, uncovered
a highly complex story by turning to Rudyard Kipling's dear old friends
– the "six honest serving-men…whose names are What and Why, and
When and How, and Where and Who". These six monosyllables, the basis
of much scientific as well as journalistic inquiry, drive storytelling of all
kinds – from fact to fiction. They are a means of framing primary and
supplementary questions and developing answers.

Media interviewees can also use them to anticipate questions and to
develop answers, but many don't bother. They just "wing it". A world
authority in the *Panorama* programme clearly believed that his illustrious
career was preparation enough for any TV interview. He reminded me of
fictional psychologist Robert Hartley's appearance on a Chicago breakfast
TV show.[2] Played by Bob Newhart, Hartley gives no forethought to the
interview and even talks about "winging it" just before the cameras roll. A
public relations opportunity becomes a humiliating disaster.

This was comedy, but real life today isn't that different. Imagine the
telephone ringing and a reporter saying: "I'd really appreciate it if you could
help me. All I need to know is …" The answer may be straightforward.
You may be expecting the call, you may have prepared for it extensively
and know exactly what to say. Alternatively, your reputation could hang in
the balance of a brief, unexpected conversation with a stranger. Feeling
at ease on the phone, some people say things they'd never say in the alien
atmosphere of a TV studio. Inappropriate responses to media interview
requests probably account for more disastrous outcomes than any other
single factor – and also for more missed opportunities. Use this checklist
to evaluate media interview requests. [Please read it even if you routinely
refer media calls to a press officer.][3]

Questions for the journalist (or researcher or producer)
If you don't know, ask:
Who recommended me? OR How did you get my name?
Why do you want to interview me specifically?
What's the story? What's the main area you want to cover?

Find out how the journalist sees the story. Are they pursuing a particular angle? Conversely, they may want your ideas. Many initial journalistic inquiries [and interviews] are like fishing trips, with the journalist casting the "hook" in the water at different points to find a strong bite. Radio/TV reporters or researchers may also want to know how you sound or look or both.

Who else have you spoken to?
This may indicate the "angle" or thrust of the story, although the reporter may not know what that will be at this stage or may not want to say.

How long will the interview be?
You may not get a precise answer. You should get an approximation. Typical telephone interviews take between five and ten minutes. A three-or four-minute recorded radio or TV interview may be reduced to a ten-to 15-second clip. You may dread a live interview, but the great advantage is that it cannot be edited. [True, it may be edited for subsequent bulletins. Working with the media does mean surrendering some professional control.]

What will the interview involve?
Possibilities include a telephone or face-to-face interview; a prime-time slot on national radio or TV news; or with a panel of speakers on a magazine programme. Don't underestimate the potential impact of a small local radio or newspaper interview. It could go global in seconds via Twitter.

When will the interview take place?
A broadcaster may provide transport to and from the studio to ensure you are there on time.

Where will the interview take place?
Allow for set-up time for an interview in your office. An empty adjacent room may be less disruptive if a TV crew wants to move furniture to create a particular effect or space for lights. An internal location may be better than an external one you cannot control. Experienced broadcast journalists may be used to the background of traffic or other noise: you may find this distracting. For more on interview locations, see Chapter Six: *Making an impression.*

Who will interview me?
[If someone other than the interviewer calls.]

When is your deadline?
Respect the deadline if you want to be in the story. There is an idea that media deadlines no longer exist in the Twitter era, but there are, in effect, more deadlines than ever. Uploading of web stories can be delayed to take in last-minute additions.

Can I have your contact details?
- Name
- Job title
- Organisation
- Phone number
- Mobile
- Email address

The job title should indicate if the reporter is a specialist medical reporter.

Will what I say be on the record?
Reporters prefer named to unnamed sources: they carry more weight. If you want anonymity, request it before the interview. Standard advice is to advise interviewees never to speak to a journalist off the record, but in the real world journalists obtain a lot of information off the record. The following terms mean different things to different people, even to different journalists. The safest policy is to assume everything is on the record, although reporters almost always respect anonymity requests made before an interview.

This is *my* understanding of on/off the record:

On the record: Anything you say may be quoted and attributed to you by name.
Attributable: Also interpreted as meaning "on the record"; whatever is said will be attributed to you specifically.
Non-attributable: What is said may be quoted if you remain unidentified.
Off the record: This term, in particular, creates confusion. According to one interpretation, the interview will not be published, but the journalist is free to use other sources to "stand the story up". "Off the record" is also

interpreted as meaning that nothing from the interview will be published or used in any way. A third interpretation is that, like "non-attributable", the interview may be published if it is not attributed to the interviewee. Such material may be described as coming from an "official" or "unnamed" source.

Ask yourself

Why me? If you're not the right person for a particular interview, explain why and try to recommend someone else. This could help to establish an invaluable, long-term relationship. Journalists, like most of us, help people who help them. Never say "No comment'. It may sound unhelpful or as if you have something to hide – and may be reported. In the worst scenario your silence could echo around the globe.

Am I the best person? You may be the most senior person in your team, without necessarily being the best candidate for a particular interview – or any interview. The media are not for everyone, no matter how clever or distinguished they may be. A charming, charismatic surgeon confided to me: "I'm used to being in control. I don't feel in control in front of that camera." We'd been role-playing media interviews to identify potential spokespeople. Try as he might – and he tried very hard – he could not exorcise his demon. This was actually a positive outcome. He demonstrated in a confidential setting that the media were not for him – much better there than in the unforgiving glare of live television. Even if you have all the desirable attributes of the model spokesperson, you will not be available all the time. Do you have a tried and trusted team of spokespeople?

What's in it for me [or my hospital, university, charity, company...?]
There is generally everything to gain by working with journalists.
An interview may:
- Generate free publicity
- Shape or inform public opinion about healthcare issues
- Influence public behaviour
- Correct misunderstandings
- Target specific groups such as research fund holders
- Promote your institution
- Promote you
- Establish good working relationships with reporters

Possible factors against going ahead include:
- Lack of preparation time
- Risk that you may be made to look foolish
- Bad timing: for example, if talking about research prematurely may jeopardise publication in a science journal. [All journalists like exclusives, including medical journal editors.]
- Pressure or resentment from colleagues
- Any risk of a threat to you or your organisation
- Loss of professional anonymity
- Loss of professional control [you will have to put yourself in the media's hands]
- Working in an alien culture

Why now?

Topicality drives the media agenda [See Chapter Two: *The news business.*] But does the timing serve your interests or those of your work or organisation?

What's in it for the media?

The media's agenda may be totally different from yours. A good story for the *media* is one that attracts the biggest possible audience; for *patients,* it is one that tells them what they need to know about illness; for *health professionals,* it is one that increases consumer understanding; and for *charities* it is one that gets wide, sympathetic coverage, leading to greater public support for them and their research; for *companies* it is one that promotes sales or their brands or, in the case of pharmaecutical companies, "disease awareness" in the run up to the launch of a new medication. These different agendas may or may not converge.

Different interview scenarios

Celebrity health: These stories are associated with confidentiality concerns and sensationalism, but talking sensitively about a celebrity's condition – though not about the individual in question – can help to convey critical messages to large, hard-to-reach audiences.

For example, the 1985 announcement that US President Ronald Reagan had undergone bowel cancer surgery probably led to more media coverage about the condition than any other development or event. It coincided with a sharp but *transitory* rise in public interest in bowel cancer; a corresponding increase in early detection tests, resulting in increased diagnosis of early-stage colorectal cancers; and a fall in advanced disease in 1986-87, suggesting a life-saving screening effect.[4] Note the word 'transitory'. The media do not do sustained – this is true of all forms of mass communication. The world's most successful companies carry on advertising to keep their brands foremost in the public mind. Media messages and stories inevitably fade from the memory as new headlines shout for our attention. Good communicators know this and find new ways to tell old stories to repeat critical messages.

Radio or TV dramas: Many media interviews are based on radio and TV drama storylines that provide a "topical" hook for stories. A classic example is the British TV production *The Singing Detective*,[5] featuring mystery writer Philip E Marlow. Psoriatic lesions and sores cover his entire body; his hands and feet are partially crippled. The scriptwriter, the late Dennis Potter, who himself had psoriasis, wrote with a pen tied to his fist, just like the fictional Marlow. This story had mass appeal even though psoriasis affects only two to three per cent of the population.

A policy announcement by government or a representative body: The media may seek a range of specialist reactions to such announcements. Some bodies get significantly more good publicity than others from these announcements. This doesn't happen by chance, but by advanced planning, anticipating opportunities and getting the right people in the right place at the right time.

Journal papers: You may be approached by the media as an expert in your field to comment on the forthcoming publication of a paper in a journal. This may help to promote you and your institution or company. Ask the journalist for an embargoed copy of the paper and any accompanying press release.

Launch of a new agent or new technology: The announcement of a new discovery or the launch of a new treatment may enhance the status of researchers and healthcare professionals. But various prominent researchers, including Lord Winston, professor of science and society at Imperial College London, have warned of the risk, particularly in competitive, high-profile areas, of even honourable experts losing objectivity when promoting their work.[6]

This can encourage an unconscious conspiracy between science and the media. Both parties want research to be reported in the best possible light – scientists to secure further funding and journalists to achieve prominence – but megaphone science, as it has been called, can create false expectations. It is also questionable now that so many university researchers are company directors or shareholders in biotech start-ups. Publicity arising from megaphone science can boost share prices.[7]

Health scares: The media are alleged to create health scares to provoke panic and to generate banner headlines. There is some truth in these claims, but they mask a phenomenon that whips up more alarm than the media ever could. The head-on collision between two of the biggest drivers in contemporary life – science and preoccupation with risk – poses many more questions than answers. Previous generations did not ask: Do cell/mobile phones cause brain cancer? Does living near high-voltage power lines cause cancer? Should people take aspirin to avoid heart attacks or will it cause bleeding ulcers? Should we vaccinate our children?

Such questions stimulate legitimate public debate, but they also foment scares that, in turn, discourage healthcare professionals from working with the media. Alas, sidestepping media questions for fear that they may exacerbate public alarm may have the opposite effect, opening up the ground to commercial interests who exploit fear for profit; and to pressure groups that disseminate misleading information. Whereas pressure groups, such as the anti-vaccination lobby, are vociferous, many healthcare professionals are the very opposite. I make no excuse for reiterating that this does not help in a world where the media may react to those who shout loudest.

Crisis: Within the context of this book a crisis is an issue or problem involving adverse publicity or threat of it. Healthcare crises include life-threatening incidents, unexpected deaths, health scares, environmental threats and scandal involving fraud and professional misconduct. Media handling of most crises is dealt with at corporate or governmental level, but local crises frequently put clinicians in the media spotlight. For example, a lead psychiatrist may be asked to comment on the community care of a patient with schizophrenia accused of murder. Good crisis management at national and local level starts with a low threshold of crisis definition[8] and a *prompt* active as distinct from reactive response.

Request for a patient interviewee: It may be better to refer journalists requesting patient interviewees to self-help groups, many of whom maintain media panels of patients. Potential pitfalls for patient media interviewees are covered in Chapter Ten: *Media Case Histories*.

Whistleblowing
Of all media interviews, few are as high-risk as those undertaken by whistleblowers. Whistleblowing involves someone revealing inside information about serious wrongdoing to a third party or parties. In theory healthcare professionals should be free to communicate concerns about poor care. In practice whistleblowers typically face condemnation not commendation. Caught up in a culture of fear they are often ignored, discouraged, ostracised and victimised, despite employers who pay lip service to the concept of an open and transparent workplace culture.

There is a common perception that a large proportion of whistleblowers turn to the media, but a UK report suggests that only 0.5 per cent do so. Published in 2013 by the whistleblowing charity Public Concern at Work, and the University of Greenwich work and employment relations unit, it was based on the experiences of 1,000 whistleblowers, 15 per cent of whom worked in healthcare. The report, *Whistleblowing: the Inside Story,* was so called to emphasise that most whistleblowers do not raise their concerns externally. The survey findings, which will resonate with health and medical whistleblowers all over the world, suggest that:

- 15 per cent of whistleblowers raise a concern externally.
- 74 per cent of whistleblowers say nothing is done about the alleged wrongdoing.
- The most likely response [19 per cent] is formal action [disciplinary or demotion].
- 15 per cent of whistleblowers are dismissed.
- Senior whistleblowers are more likely to be dismissed.
- Newer employees are most likely to blow the whistle.
- 39 per cent of whistleblowers have less than two years experience.

CASE HISTORY

Dr Steve Bolsin began working as a consultant paediatric anaesthetist at Bristol Royal Infirmary in the UK in 1988. From his first day the length of heart operations concerned him. Subsequently he alerted the chief executive to the high mortality rate in babies having heart surgery. This provoked a hostile response – he was told that "this was not the way to get on in Bristol".

He blew the whistle, provoking one of Britain's biggest healthcare scandals, which was taken up by *Private Eye,* the leading satirical magazine. Two doctors were struck off the medical register and another was suspended, but Bolsin was unable to continue working in the UK. He made a successful career in Australia. In 2013 he returned to the UK to receive the Royal College of Anaesthesia Medal for promoting safety in anaesthesia.

This might seem to be an extreme case, but whistleblowing is widely associated with lost jobs, shattered careers, split families and divorce. For example, the British paediatrician Dr Kim Holt had to wait four years to get her job back after whistleblowing in 2007 about staffing levels in a children's clinic and other issues. In 2011 she established Patients First, a network of health professionals supporting whistleblowers in the NHS. In 2014 she took up a temporary secondment with the Care Quality Commission, the independent regulator of health and social care in England.

Whistleblowers who go to the media need to be aware that they may lose control of the story once it is in the public domain. They also need to establish ground rules. Are they speaking on or off the record? What does the reporter understand by these terms – they are interpreted in different ways. These questions are discussed in this chapter on pages 42 and 43.

Many countries have bodies for whistleblowers such as the UK's Public Concern at Work [above].The Whistleblowing International Network website, on July 2, 2015, included details of organisations in Austria, Canada, Germany, Guatemala, Holland, Ireland, Italy, Poland, Russia, South Africa, the UK and the USA. Founder members of whistleblowers. org.au in Australia included the late psychiatrist Dr Jean Lennane. She became a whistleblower in 1990, after being sacked when she publicly criticised cuts to mental health and drug and alcohol services.

Press releases

Many media interviews are based on press releases. These are distributed to the media to launch products, businesses, books and to promote events and journal papers. There are three ways you may become involved with press releases. First, you may be invited as an independent expert to comment on a press release about new research in your field. Second, you may be invited to contribute to and check a press release about your own research.

Press releases are a legitimate way to disseminate news and information, but many are just blatant pieces of marketing masquerading as news. A press release should be newsworthy, but of 269 press releases I received as medical correspondent of *The Observer* in a fortnight in August 1998, only two met this basic standard. [I collected them all in a box in my own mini research project.] Millions of working hours are frittered away compiling useless press releases that, for example, tell us yet again that the contraceptive pill may affect mood and sexuality.

So why are journalists inundated with press releases? Perhaps because, from time to time, they actually use them for the wrong reasons. The *BMJ's* senior news editor, Annabel Ferriman, a former national newspaper correspondent, explained: "It is very easy, if you are up against a deadline, simply to reproduce a press release, without giving it the scrutiny you should. I have seen press releases reproduced almost verbatim by journalists. For example, a particularly idiosyncratic example was reproduced word for word in *The Guardian.* In this case, not many people would find it sinister. But it shows how easy it can be to manipulate the press."[9]

Again, I would like to stress that press releases are a legitimate communication tool. Leading journals regularly set the medical news agenda by distributing press releases about studies they are publishing, as we saw with the uptake of stories by *The Times* and *The Sun,* in the study referred to in Chapter Two: *The news business.* This study also found that coverage in these newspapers from 1,193 research articles in *The Lancet* and *BMJ* was restricted to papers accompanied by press releases.[10] Why do journals distribute press releases? First, press releases can generate public debate about critical health issues. Second, media coverage of research articles can increase journal circulation and advertising revenue – many medical journals are commercial enterprises just like radio and TV stations.

Common questions about press releases include:

What is the difference between a press release and an advertisement? The media do not charge for publishing the substance of press releases, but they reserve the right to edit or reject them. Advertisers, in contrast, retain total control over space or airtime they buy.

How many press releases are published? This varies according to the daily news agenda. A big international story such as Hurricane Katrina in 2005, or Hurricane Sandy in 2012 will dominate the news, "killing" most of the estimated 2,000 press releases a day distributed by agencies such as PR Newswire and Business Wire.

Why are there so many press releases? News is perceived to be more credible than advertising. There is a popular, much quoted idea that five times more people will read an article than an advertisement. I have been unable to verify it.

What will happen if I am asked to contribute to a press release? A press officer should establish how you see the story, check the facts and figures and may request a direct quotation. Direct quotations in science stories can bring a human dimension to a mass of numbers.

Can I check the release? If you contribute you should be consulted, but don't try to rewrite it – your way may not be the media's. Formulaic press releases work best.

Will the media contact me directly about the release? They may request an interview or seek additional information or clarification. The release – if you agree – may include your contact details. Alternatively, a press officer may take initial calls and brief you accordingly.

Will I be on radio and TV? Most of today's big stories will be on radio and TV, but most media interviews are done by phone. The likelihood of a story being broadcast may depend on aural or visual appeal. For example, a piece about music therapy could make good radio; a story about art therapy good TV. However you are interviewed, preparation is critical. We turn to preparation next.

SUMMARY

- Inappropriate responses to media interview requests probably account for more disastrous outcomes than any other single factor.
- There is generally everything to gain by working with journalists, but there are many reasons for not proceeding with an interview.
- You may be the most senior member of your team without necessarily being the best person to do a particular interview – or any interview.
- There is a risk, particularly in competitive high-profile areas, that even well-intentioned experts may lose objectivity when reporting their work.
- Press releases are a legitimate way to disseminate news and information, but many are just blatant pieces of marketing masquerading as news.

NOTES AND REFERENCES

1 *The Opren Scandal* (1983) Screened January 17. BBC TV. Opren was withdrawn from worldwide markets in 1982.

2 *The Bob Newhart Show* (1975) *Who is Mr. X?* 20th Century Fox.

3 Press officers are the main point of contact between the media and organisations ranging from multinational corporations to charities and government agencies. They are responsible for preparing, writing and distributing press releases; briefing media spokespeople; organising press conferences and briefings, and liaising with journalists.

4 Brown ML, Potosky AL (1990) The presidental effect: the public health response to media coverage about Ronald Reagan's colon cancer episode *Public Opinion Quarterly.* 54 (3): 317-29

5 Potter D (1986) *The Singing Detective* was first screened in the UK by the BBC in 1986. It ranks 20th in the British Film Institute's list of the 100 greatest TV programmes.

6 Winston R (2008) Beware the robodocs *New Scientist* 199 Issue 2,670 118. August 20

7 Rose S (2004) This theme was explored by Professor Steven Rose, then head of the UK Open University brain and behaviour research group, in a talk at the Edinburgh Science Festival.

8 Bland M (1998) *Communicating Out of a Crisis* p5 MacMillan Business

9 Ferriman A (1998) Pitfalls of medical journalism pp1 & 8 *HealthWatch* newsletter 28, January 1998

10 Bartlett C, Sterne J, Egger M (2002) What is newsworthy? Longitudinal study of the reporting of medical research in two British newspapers *BMJ* 325 pp 81-84

Chapter 4

Preparing for a media interview

Read this chapter to find out about:

DEFINING YOUR OBJECTIVES

DEVELOPING MESSAGES

ANTICIPATING QUESTIONS

ANSWERING QUESTIONS

Many clinicians and scientists give successful media interviews with little if any preparation, but governments, large companies, hospital groups, research institutes and medical charities regard preparation as essential. It is easy to see why: interviews can and do go wrong; medicine and the media are disparate cultures; and fragmentation of the media has created new pitfalls. One ill-advised comment can go viral and reach millions of people in an instant. Preparation often includes formal training, without which many prominent people lack the skills and confidence to make the most of interview opportunities.

Beyond the media

This book is about handling the media, but much of it, especially this chapter, describes approaches that can also be used in other settings such as Q and A sessions after talks, one-to-one meetings and even job interviews. For example, acting against advice from academic colleagues who insisted that students rarely won such hearings, I used these techniques to prepare my younger son, Chris, for a university appeal in a dispute over his degree.

We developed key messages, anticipated questions and framed answers. We worked on possible supplementary questions and answers. We worked on eye contact and body language. We spent four hours refining and rehearsing – successfully.

He returned from the fray and said: "Thanks very much, Dad. It was exactly as you said it would be." In fact, it was a joint effort. You don't have to be an expert to make these techniques work. Nor, normally, would you need so long to prepare for an interview.

Know your audience

Chris knew his audience unlike, for example, many television news interviewees. Unlike newspapers that target readership according to socio-political groupings, television is directed at broad audiences. The need is for simple, clear and direct language that must be neither too intellectual nor insult the intelligence. Interviews for healthcare professionals may be less challenging. Interviewees may have a better idea about what their colleagues know, what they need to know, what they believe and what they will accept.

Defining your objectives

Start with the end in mind.[1] What do you want the audience to do and what will you have to do to make it happen? To communicate successfully – to achieve change – means doing one or more of the following:

- Informing
- Teaching
- Motivating
- Persuading
- Inspiring
- Promoting
- Entertaining

Chris had to persuade.

Developing messages

Effective messages are catalysts of change. Alas, many key messages are laid low by imprecise thinking, long sentences, Latin terminology, verbosity, abstractions and exclamations, platitudes, euphemisms and clichés. Examples from the University of the Bleeding Obvious include "People are our best resource" and "Positive personal chances can enhance health".

Knowing what you want from the audience helps to develop change-generating messages. The best ones are short and snappy – statements of fact or advice or a call to arms. Short ones are easier to say and remember. Twitter [140 characters] set a new gold standard.

Effective messages are built up around:

Simplicity: This is the ultimate communication challenge: "Make things as simple as possible, but no simpler." [Attributed to Albert Einstein.]

The first health key messages were encapsulated in the decanted wisdom of proverbs. The classic examples overleaf combine brevity and simplicity with elegance and impact.

- Let food be thy medicine and medicine be thy food [Hippocrates]
- Light meals ensure a long life [Scottish]
- The best doctors are Dr Diet, Dr Quiet and Dr Merryman [English]
- Diet takes better care of you than the scalpel [Spanish]
- A slender diet chases illness [Arabic]
- Early to bed, early to rise, makes a man healthy, wealthy and wise [American]
- Up at five, dine at nine, sup at five, bed at nine, will make you live to 99 [French]
- After dinner rest a while, after supper walk a mile [Latin]
- A drachm of prudence is worth a bushel of medicine [Lebanese]
- For a long life and good health, eat like a cat and drink like a dog [German]
- Long meals mean a short life, short meals mean a long life [Italian]
- Cleanliness is next to godliness [Hebrew]
- Take running water at its source [Spanish]
- Give green fruit and unshaven men a wide berth [Spanish]
- A merry heart doeth good like a medicine [Proverbs, 17. 22]

Try to say as much as anyone of these proverbs in the same number or fewer words. A copywriting career beckons if you succeed.

Surprise: As media messages today these proverbs would have limited impact. Tell editors that "light meals ensure a long life" and they might say, "Tell me something I don't know. *Surprise me.*" Surprise commands attention. It can make us feel *alive.* Conversely, rather like an adolescent with a nagging mum, we feel numb if we hear the same message time and time again. We are more responsive to the new or unexpected.

Alas many core healthcare messages need repeating again and again. They include nothing surprising or new. For example, the evidence for childhood vaccination is overwhelming, but the benefits still need emphasising – ironically because vaccination has been so successful. How many 25-year-old Western parents have seen a case of measles?

How can we inject the power of surprise into vaccination appeals to parents?

As related in the previous chapter children's author Roald Dahl, whose seven-year-old daughter Olivia died from measles, succeeded with: "Not to vaccinate your child really is almost a crime."[2] "Twinning" disparate words – such as "vaccination" and "crime" – is an old poetic and book-titling trick. For example, the title alone helped to make Desmond Morris's *The Naked Ape*[3] an overnight bestseller. Sales topped half a million within months – remarkable for a book on human biology. They may not have topped 1,000 if it had been called Human Biology. Word twinning is also evident in film titles such as *Eyes Wide Shut, True Lies,* and *A Hard Day's Night.*

Dahl's status as an international celebrity also helped, but more importantly he had a way with words and he knew that most parents – vaccination opponents included – want the best for their kids. Suggesting that some parents were akin to criminal made headlines and became a talking point on radio and TV and in pubs and cafés. Healthcare professionals may not want to be so provocative. Softly softly can work just as well. For example, the late Professor Eric Wilkes allayed public concern about pressure on beds by describing UK hospices as places where "there isn't a parking meter on the end of the bed". Parking meters and hospices had probably never before been seen together in the same sentence.

Of course, this kind of juxtaposition cannot be written into all key messages, and not all key messages have to surprise. Some even work because they are so predictable. The former British Prime Minister Margaret Thatcher's most famous soundbite ["You turn if you want to; the lady's not for turning"][4] defined her as the "the Iron Lady" of British politics. It worked because it was precisely what the audience, her party, the Conservatives, wanted to hear. It caught the political mood of the moment in a precise and calculated way, resonating with the audience's values and aspirations.

Emotion: Dahl's vaccination message had powerful emotional appeal because his child died before a measles vaccine became available and because it included the word "your". "You" and "your" address us directly and reach out to our emotions. "You" is widely reported to be one of the most effective words in advertising.

Many healthcare messages lack these "Y" words, perhaps because scientifically-orientated spokespeople veer away from the emotional to adopt a detached scientific stance. Detachment may be perceived as coldness. Connecting with an audience on an emotional level is more likely to make people care; the more they care the more likely they are to act. It is not enough to report unequivocal results from the very best randomised clinical trials. Evidence-based medicine will not speak for itself to consumer audiences. It needs a nudge. Hollow shells of professionalism do not make good communicators.

In broadcast interviews consumer audiences may react less to the scientific substance of what is said and more to their perception of the substance of the interviewee. They may make snap judgements about trust, integrity and how they would feel if the interviewee were their doctor.

Students used to be taught that there were two types of audience: intellectual and emotional. The intellectual audience was reportedly more interested in the big picture, as presented, for example, in statistics; and the emotional one in specific examples, as presented in case histories and stories, as discussed below. In practice the emotional and intellectual overlap.

Relevance: You may be enthralled by the science of medicine; most consumers are not. Sad but true – a big loss for them. Their interest is restricted to benefits and outcomes. Some scientists cannot understand why non-scientists do not share their enthusiasm for, say, the properties of adenine and thymine, but even their [or your] scientific interest may be limited. A new gas cooker, for example, may incorporate months of prize-winning R and D, but are you really interested in how the gas reaches the saucepan or how the designer has cleverly varied the intensity of the heat? Your concern may be restricted to whether or not it is safe, cost efficient and pleasing to the eye – to outcomes.

Stories: Key messages don't work in isolation. They need well-balanced stories to make them relevant, to give them context and meaning to help us to define and compare ourselves with others – to give us a sense of perspective about our place in the scheme of things. Analogies, third-party endorsements, personal experiences, statistics and easy-to-understand images inject life into stories. For example, talking about a 324-metre-tall structure will mean nothing to most people: saying that it is "as high the Eiffel Tower" gives it context and vivid immediacy. A patient describing a severe physical handicap as "living with the handbrake on" resonated with me.

News values: The richer a story is in news values, the more likely it is to be published by traditional media. News values [see Chapter Two: *The news business*] include novelty, universality, topicality, emotion and controversy.

We shall see later how patient groups' and charities' use of new media has challenged the monopoly of the news-values culture – anyone can now publish a story or a key message. However, news values remain important because traditional media reach out to millions of people and because news values also drive a lot of new media. News values, despite claims to the contrary, are not just a part of our time and culture. They have evolved over centuries in what is, in effect, a continuous trial in which primary end points are now expressed in sales – and, increasingly, hits.

The power of three: You could put across nine or ten different points or messages in a five-minute interview, only for them to be quickly forgotten. Restrict yourself to three points at most because human beings are very good at conceptualising and remembering things in threes. For example:

- Breakfast, lunch, dinner
- Beginning, middle, end
- Left, right, centre
- Up, down, middle
- Past, present, future
- Problem, cause, solution
- Win, lose, draw
- ABC
- Morning, noon, night

The conventional wisdom is that if you have three key messages, and deliver each one three times in different ways, the audience may remember one or two, so long as they are *relevant*. As the Latin phrase has it –*omne trium perfectum* – everything that comes in threes is perfect.

The mental eye-line: Imagine your messages literally sticking out in front of your head. Locking them into this mental eye-line keeps them in view and will help to keep the interview on track. Lose sight of them and the interview may go off at a tangent of the reporter's choosing if you are fielding a barrage of questions.

Three-dimensional thinking: This helps to develop change-generating messages. The one-dimensional media interviewee thinks: what's in for me? The three-dimensional interviewee thinks: first, what's in it for the journalist? Second, what's in it for the audience? And only then, what's in it for me?

Anticipating questions: It is relatively easy to deliver messages from a script, not so easy in the cut and thrust of an interview. Anticipating the questions makes it easier. It is worth reiterating here Rudyard Kipling's brilliant summary[5] of the basis of scientific and journalistic enquiry, which provides the definitive checklist, known as the six Ws, even though it includes an H.

"I keep six honest serving-men,
[They taught me all I knew]
Their names are What, and Why, and When
And How and Where and Who."

There is a tragic similarity between Kipling and the previously mentioned Roald Dahl. Both lost their first girl child, and though they were left distraught, both wrote dazzlingly for children.

The Kiplings' daughter Josephine died of pneumonia, aged six, in 1899, while Dahl's daughter Olivia died from measles encephalitis, aged seven, in 1962. Kipling dreamed up the *Just So stories* for Josephine. He had previously written *The Jungle Book* for her, as a hand-inscribed first edition reveals. Dahl in his turn dedicated the *BFG* to Olivia.

I prepared these media questions for a mental health charity bipolar disorder workshop:

- What is bipolar disorder?
- What is manic depression?
- How many people have it?
- Are some people more susceptible than others or can anyone get it?
- When does it start?
- What are the symptoms?
- How does it impact on people's quality of life?
- Does it make people unreliable in the workplace?
- How is it treated? [Could be the first of several questions.]
- What's the difference between typical and atypical antipsychotic medications?
- What about the side effects of pharmacological treatment?
- What about complementary therapies?
- What about psychological therapies such as cognitive behavioural therapy?
- How does it affect you specifically?
- Do you feel as if you are in control of your illness?
- Are there any specific steps you take to control your illness?
- Have you ever been sacked as a result of your illness?
- Have you ever contemplated suicide?
- What treatment do you take?
- How good are doctors at recognising and treating bipolar affective disorder?

Questions such as "Have you ever contemplated suicide?'" and "Have you ever been sacked as a result of your illness?" may seem hard or intrusive and insensitive, but almost every *anticipated* question is a potential opportunity, just as, in the words of the cliché, every crisis is an opportunity. We will return later to the suicide question.

The "tougher" the interview, the more credit for getting it right. This is why seasoned politicians seek interviews with rough, tough anchors. You may have heard or read reports of 50 media interviews in the past two weeks, but how many do you actually remember? How many have you forgotten completely? You're more likely to recall the tough ones.

So don't just anticipate "easy" questions. Think of the dreaded ones, the ones you should get from a halfway-competent journalist. Work out the answers. Speak them as well as think them, preferably with someone listening or, even better, role-playing the journalist. Speaking will help to refine and simplify. Thinking an answer without speaking it is like rehearsing a play by only thinking the lines. Does this mean a media interview is a "performance"? Yes. You are talking to "an audience". Do you have to be word perfect? No. Unless you are a professional actor you will almost certainly sound stilted if you stick rigidly to a script. Just know what you want to say. Make sure it's something new for the audience – or, if it's something old, say it in a new way, like Roald Dahl.

There is a big difference between a media interview and everyday conversation, however much the former may sometimes sound like the latter. Talking routinely with friends or colleagues we may not be on our guard. We don't have to anticipate. We may take time to weigh up thoughts. We may even talk throughout this critical thinking process, the verbal equivalent of treading water, with our legs pumping just to stay still. We may not be at our most coherent. We may even contradict ourselves, but we may still finally take credit for a considered reply. In contrast, pump away in a media interview and you will look weak and indecisive – and waste time. Get straight to the point.

In everyday conversation we also have the luxury of instant feedback. We can adjust or qualify the things we say in response to, say, the shuffle of feet, a bewildered expression or raised eyebrows. Media interviews are directed at invisible audiences, making it all the more important to meet the Einstein challenge by keeping things as simple and as clear as possible.

Also be as succinct as possible. As I said [Chapter Three: *Responding to a media interview request*], most media telephone interviews take between five and ten minutes. Broadcast interviews tend to be shorter. A three-minute interview might run to about 400 words, 150 from the interviewer. By way of comparison this paragraph contains 56 words.

Try this exercise. Create an interview scenario and sum up what you want to say in 300 words, then 200, then 100. Alternatively, imagine yourself in a lift talking to someone who will be getting out at the third floor. Put your message(s) across before they leave – in, say, ten to 20 seconds.

Check that you can articulate your message without notes. Recite it to a friend or colleague. Ask them to repeat it back. Change it if what they say is easier to understand – which sometimes happens. Check if they can still remember it an hour later and the following day – without priming them that you are going to check.

The forgetting curve described by the German psychologist Hermann Ebbinghaus[6] (1850-1906) suggests we forget a significant amount of information within 20 minutes:

Time period	Percentage of knowledge retained
20 minutes	60%
1 hour	45%
9 hours	38%
2 days	30%
6 days	23%

There are severe limitations to this research, the most significant being that Ebbinghaus was the only subject in the study and that some topics – for example, fundamental issues about life and death – are more likely to stick in our minds than others. Nonetheless his influence has been far reaching.

Your audience's recall of what you say will depend upon the clarity and power of your storytelling and messages and the interview techniques you use to communicate them – this takes us to the next chapter.

SUMMARY

- Good communication generates change by doing one or more of the following – informing, teaching, motivating, persuading, inspiring, promoting, entertaining.
- Remember the power of three. People are good at conceptualising and remembering things in three. For example, breakfast, lunch, dinner; beginning, middle, end; left, right, centre; past, present, future.
- Messages do not work in isolation. They need well-balanced stories to make them resonate. Analogies, third-party endorsements, personal experience and easy-to-understand images can bring stories to life.
- Try to think like a journalist, anticipating the questions they will ask.
- Work out the answers and rehearse them by speaking not just thinking them. Thinking through an answer without speaking it is like rehearsing a play by only thinking the lines.

NOTES AND REFERENCES

[1] Covey S (1989) "Begin with the end in mind" is habit two of The 7 Habits of Highly Effective People Simon and Schuster

[2] Dahl R (1988) Dahl wrote the appeal for the UK Sandwell Health Authority in the West Midlands.

[3] Morris D (1967) The Naked Ape, Bantam Books/ Jonathan Cape

[4] Thatcher M (1980) Conservative Party Conference, Brighton, October 10.

[5] Kipling R (1902) Opening lines of poem accompanying The Elephant's Child

[6] Ebbinghaus H (1885) Über das Gedächtnis (On Memory), later translated to English as Memory. A Contribution to Experimental Psychology

Chapter 5

Different types of interview

Read this chapter to find out about:

THE COLLABORATIVE/INFORMATIONAL INTERVIEW

THE PEP (POINT, EXAMPLE, POINT) INTERVIEW

THE BRIDGE INTERVIEW

THE TURNING-SCIENCE-UPSIDE-DOWN INTERVIEW

THE EMAIL INTERVIEW

These approaches should not be seen as independent entities. The first four may all be used in a single interview if, for example, a collaborative interview becomes confrontational.

Collaborative/informational
The most common type of interview in medical and healthcare reporting: the interviewee responds to questions with points and messages.

PEP (point, example, point)
Collaborative interviews benefit from PEP. The interviewee makes a point, backs it up with a specific example and message and then repeats the process. In communication of any kind, general statements tend to be weak while specific statements and examples are strong.

"Bridging" – the ABC of communication
The above techniques can work well if the interviewer and interviewee have the same agenda. But what if they don't – often more likely – and the questions take you away from your agenda? Bridging can get you back on track.

It includes:
Acknowledge
Bridge
Communicate

Acknowledging a question involves taking a word or phrase from it and creating a verbal bridge to a point you want to communicate. For example:
Acknowledgement: "You say that, but that's not quite right…"
Bridge: "What we feel is that…"
Communicate: You make your point and deliver your message (s)

Or:
Acknowledgement: "I don't know about that…
Bridge: "What I do know is that…"
Communicate: Point or message.

Bridging will not necessarily make you sound like a politician – a common concern. There are legitimate reasons for adopting it. For example, imagine a TV interview with a physician about a new campaign to encourage adherence or concordance among hypertensive patients. It coincides with the launch of a controversial report about animal use in medical research. A press officer forewarns the physician that this could distract attention from hypertension. Sure enough, the reporter's first question is: "Before we talk about high blood pressure, can you tell us what you think about this highly controversial report, which claims that animals are being needlessly sacrificed in animal research."

This example shows that it is not enough to know your subject and messages. Knowing how to navigate to them is just as important. Our fictional physician reaches his destination thus:

Acknowledgement: "I haven't seen this report, so I cannot comment on it specifically. Moreover, I'm not an expert in this field, but I do know that animal testing is a legal requirement in many instances.
Bridge: "I want to talk about what *I do know about* – treating high blood pressure, or hypertension…
Communicate: "The right kind of treatment can prevent many premature deaths."

The preceding chapter listed possible media questions for spokespeople for a bipolar disorder charity. These included "Have you ever contemplated suicide?" Possible answers below illustrate the power of bridging. The first two answers are non-bridging ones.

1. "No comment."

2. "I don't want to talk about that. This is a strictly personal issue and I regard this question as extremely intrusive."

Compare these negative replies that shut down the dialogue with the following bridges that open it up.

Acknowledgment: "Yes, I have contemplated suicide."
Bridge: "But as you can see I'm alive, in no small part thanks to the charity. I'd like to tell you how it helped me and how it could help many of your viewers."
Communicate: Key message…

Or:
Acknowledgment: "No, I haven't contemplated suicide."
Bridge: "But what matters are the many people who have, and what our charity can do to help them. I'd like to tell you how…"
Communicate: Key message…

This example also underlines the importance of anticipating questions, as discussed on page 60. Deciding on live TV whether or not to discuss a suicidal history would not be smart. This is an extreme example, but if you have to think your way through any part of a spoken interview, it will suggest you are under-prepared. In anticipating questions, think of the ones you most dread. These may be the ones you are most likely to get. There is no such thing as a hard question if you have anticipated it and prepared a good answer, but an "easy" question may be hard if you haven't.

Lack of preparation can provoke snap "no comment" answers that may suggest you have something to hide. I cannot say too often: never say "No comment". There are four acceptable ways to answer all questions:

- Directly, with or without a bridge
- Explaining that you don't have the answer, but that you will get it
- Explaining that you do have the answer but cannot discuss it because…
- Explaining that the question is outside your area of expertise.

Option three is acceptable only if the answer would breach confidentiality or national security; or if it involves an unresolved court case or (though journalists might not accept this) commercially sensitive information; or extremely personal intrusive questioning of no public interest. What an interviewee may deem to be commercially sensitive a reporter may argue is the public interest. But whatever the situation, "no comment" is never an acceptable way to hide an awkward, uncomfortable truth. The sooner you come clean, the more likely it will be on your terms, not someone else's.

Recommend someone else if the question is outside your expertise. Don't be afraid to admit you don't know the answer. Bridge to what you do know. For example, "I only wish I knew. I might have a Nobel Prize if I did, but what I can tell you is…"

Turning science upside down

The traditional way of telling a scientific story is to start with the history and background before discussing the current situation and offering a conclusion. The media turn the science upside down and start with the conclusion. Yes, the *scientific conclusion* becomes the *journalistic introduction* or intro.

Many researchers put too much initial emphasis in media interviews on background or methodology because this is how they begin to tell scientific stories. These bits are of least interest to most journalists and result in interviewers steering the conversation towards benefits and outcomes by asking: "What does this mean for the patient?"

This is a classic example of traditional scientific storytelling via two "key messages". The first six sentences may have seemed important to the author but risk leaving an interviewer cold.

Key message one
"Bone health is extremely important to quality of life."
Journalistic reaction: tell me something I don't know.
"Healthy bones provide the frame that promotes mobility and protects against injury."
Journalistic reaction: When are they going to get to the point?
"Bones store minerals that are critical to the operation of many other life-sustaining systems in the body."
Journalistic reaction: I'm not here for an elementary biology lesson.
"Unhealthy bones adversely affect these other functions and can lead to debilitating fractures."
Journalistic reaction: Please don't patronise me.
Key message two
"The bone health of Americans seems to be in peril. Left unchecked it is going to get worse as the population ages."
Journalistic reaction: What's the current situation?

"Each year some 1.5 million American citizens have an osteoporotic-related fracture."
Journalistic reaction: At last, the story – an intro!

Having to listen to six sentences about an issue of such fundamental importance to the quality of life of millions of people may not seem irksome. It sets the scene. And surely journalists have patience enough to absorb them? Yes – but imagine having to scan dozens of such examples every week in the hundreds of press releases clogging up your in box. What makes the second message work for the jaded journalist? It gets straight to the point, flags up a specific problem for millions of people, puts it into context with a statistical estimate and warns that things will get worse if nothing is done. It is a call for action of personal interest to many people.

The email interview
An interview is by traditional understanding a face-to-face encounter – though we have to come to understand it, also, as voice to voice when it involves two people talking via telephone or microphone. However, email has opened up another way of exchanging questions and answers, of which journalists are increasingly taking advantage. It somewhat denies the interviewer the chance to establish a rapport with the interviewee –or, for that matter, to put them on the spot – but it gives both parties time to consider their responses. It also throws up ethical issues and has pros and cons, as discussed below.

The email interview became controversial when Fred Vogelstein of *Wired* magazine asked Jason Calacanis, a blogging pioneer, and Dave Winer, an internet pioneer, for telephone interviews.[1] They both laid down conditions. Calacanis insisted on doing the interview via email so that he could publish it in full online. Winer said that he would answer the questions, in public, on his blog.

Both men complained that previously they had been misquoted. Scott Rosenberg, founder of Salon.com, complained that reporters used the traditional interview to prod, wheedle, cajole and possibly trip up interviewees. He claimed that any reporter who didn't admit this was lying, either to his listener or himself.[2] There are, of course, times when reporters should challenge interviewees, even if it means prodding and wheedling, but what are the pros and cons of email interviews?

An email interview may be productive:
- When a reporter is trying to clarify complex technical information. No one can claim misquotation, although quotes could still be taken out of context.
- When an interviewee thinks through his answers in a considered, otherwise impossible way. [Why shouldn't the interviewee be able to edit the words, to make them more accurate and articulate? Why should editing rights be restricted to the reporter, sub-editor et al? Isn't the email interview another expression of the democratisation of the media?]
- When logistical problems before a deadline leave no time for a traditional interview.
- When a reporter needs an answer to a straightforward question arising from an earlier interview.
- When an interviewee is better with the written than the spoken word.
- When the interviewee is deaf or too hard of hearing to be interviewed.
- When there is a language barrier.

An email interview may be counter-productive:
- When answers are incomplete and prompt supplementary questions and additional email exchanges that encroach upon deadlines.
- When an interview involves a controversial story such as alleged fraud. It may allow the alleged perpetrator to sidestep critical questions and give evasive answers.
- When it is interpreted as meaning that the interviewee has something to hide.
- When it is a substitute for a traditional interview with follow-up questions that would give a story a wider perspective.
- When it blocks free flow of information between journalists and their sources. Journalists rely on sources they can actually talk to.

This last point is critical in terms of building relationships with reporters. Imagine yourself as a reporter who needs to obtain information about a new development from one of two sources. The first is extremely accessible. The second restricts access to emails. No prizes for guessing what happens, especially if the second source's emailed answers are incomplete.

This is why reporters prefer traditional face-to-face interviews. Communication is, as we have seen, actually about far more than words. In meeting one another, people give a sense of themselves that cannot be transmitted by email. A wry smile, strong eye contact or raised eyebrows may help to put a story into context. Face-to-face contact and the accompanying body language can also convey passion or dedication or anxiety or concern more powerfully than any email.

Journalists have debated the merits of the email interview extensively in what has been an action replay of the great telephone interview debate more than a century ago. Critics maintained that it was inappropriate to gather news via this newfangled device because reporters would not really know whom they were talking to. The telephone, of course, is now as much a part of the reporter's world as a pen and notebook. The same is true of the email interview, especially in medical and science reporting with its emphasis on data. But if you are interviewing someone to write a profile or for an in-depth investigation, there is no real substitute for meeting them. And data may need to be put into context via a quote. The advantage of actually talking to or even better seeing people should become even more apparent in the next chapter.

SUMMARY

- It is not enough to know your subject and messages. Knowing how to navigate to them by using interview techniques such as "bridging" is just as important.
- There is no such thing as a hard question if you anticipate it and prepare an answer, but the "easiest" of questions may be hard if you haven't.
- Traditional scientific storytelling begins with history and background. The media turn the science upside down and start with the scientific conclusion.
- An email interview can be productive when a reporter is trying to clarify technical information but unproductive when answers are incomplete and prompt supplementary questions that encroach upon deadlines.

NOTES AND REFERENCES

1 Jarvis J (2007) The thoroughly modern interview rewrites the rules *The Guardian* May 14

2 Ibid

Chapter 6

Making an impression

Read this chapter to find out about:

THE CRITICAL IMPORTANCE OF FIRST IMPRESSIONS

TELEPHONE AND FACE-TO-FACE INTERVIEWS

RADIO AND TV INTERVIEWS

PRESS CONFERENCES

FLY-ON-THE-WALL DOCUMENTARIES

Media interviews, like radio signals, are susceptible to interference. This "noise" can include cynicism, indifference, misunderstanding, prejudice and uncontrollable distractions. For example, a reporter may see an interviewee as a stereotypical macho surgeon. Viewers might be too busy arguing to hear a word of your legendary TV interview. Granny may lose her teeth. There is nothing you can do about such things, but you can reduce noise by checking that a reporter is keeping up with you or by making them feel valued by putting yourself in their shoes.

One of my first medical interviewees was the late Lord Rosenheim, formerly professor of medicine at University College Hospital, London. As distinguished as I was undistinguished, he had an engaging smile, quiet kindness, humility, and looked me straight in the eye. It is easy to believe the obituary reports that he had no enemies. He made me feel valued. Yes, maybe he flattered me.

What does this say about journalistic objectivity? I hope I looked beyond the smile into the substance of the good lord's words, but how? Probably pretty haphazardly. I believe we all amass our own private collections of stereotypes and put individuals into one category or another. This may be unscientific, but it can be reassuring, a way of making sense of a chaotic world.

Princeton University psychologists Janine Willis and Alexander Todorov found that volunteers made judgements about people within just a tenth of a second,[1] not just about such superficial qualities as attractiveness, but also about trustworthiness, competence and likeability. Given more time to look, their opinions did not change significantly. Research also suggests that faces with spectacles are perceived to be five per cent more intelligent than the same faces without spectacles; that a slight increase in the distance between the eyes causes a person to be judged more honest and reliable; and that remarkably small changes in eyebrow height affect perceptions about intelligence.[2]

You can override first impressions to a greater or lesser extent, but not, as many healthcare professionals try to do, with a scientifically neutral tone that shouts: "I don't care!" *Visible* commitment and enthusiasm are infectious. Probably the most important factors in communication, they are frequently missing from healthcare communication and generate a lot of noise. I hope this chapter will help to turn noise down and levels of commitment and enthusiasm up.

Anyone who has read to a child knows that how you say something is as important as what you say. For example, in the story of *The Three Little Pigs*, the line "I'll HUFF and I'll PUFF and I'll BLOW your house down" cries out for the right inflection, with wave-like movements to register the highs and lows in the pitch of your voice. Inflection-free voices sound monotonous and bored.

It is a truism that we speak with our voice but communicate with our whole bodies. There are three elements in face-to-face communication: words, tone of voice and body language. The question as to how these three elements are weighted in day-to-day communication is controversial. It has been erroneously but widely reported that words account for 7%, tone of voice for 38% and body language 55%.[3] This is patently absurd, a distortion of the original research. For example, the words "Fire, fire! Get out!", will count for more than body language. The same would be true of an interviewee making controversial allegations in a prime-time TV news bulletin.

These widely quoted figures have created confusion, but the relationship between words, tone and body language in communication is nonetheless important. For example, you will get a mixed mesage if I praise you while avoiding your eyes. Conversely, you may believe me if my words and body seem to be as one.

Telephone interviews
Body language may seem to have nothing to do with telephone interviews in which voice is the sole means of communication. But body language underpins successful telephone communication. Smiling into the phone can generate warmth that will resonate in your voice, while standing up will help to project it. "Talking" with your hands or arms will underline key points.

We now spend more time texting and emailing than talking on the phone, but time, logistics and financial restraints mean that the telephone interview is as important as ever in journalism. Best for short, uncomplicated stories, it is fast and serviceable, the McDonald's of journalism, according to John Brady, author of *The Craft of Interviewing*.[4]

Familiarity with the phone means that many people treat a telephone interview like a routine conversation. They talk too fast, forgetting that the reporter is probably taking notes. Check that they are keeping up even if you perceive yourself to be a slow speaker. This should stop you talking too fast and encourage inexperienced reporters to admit if they are falling behind. Talking too fast also encourages some people to say too much. Recapping and pausing briefly after key points will help to hold your speed in check and emphasise the points. Keep answers as short as possible but as long as necessary – the better prepared you are with brief summary notes and messages, the easier this will be.

Imagining that the interview is to take place on live radio or TV may make you that little bit sharper – in the event of an actual telephone interview with a radio or TV reporter, it is important to distinguish between one to gather information and one that is to be broadcast, either recorded or live. The reporter should make it clear if the plan is to broadcast an interview.

Don't try to do anything else during a telephone interview, such as working on your PC. People sense if they haven't got your undivided attention.

Recorded telephone interviews

Many telephone interviews, of course, are recorded. This has legal implications. For example, in Britain individuals can record telephone conversations for private use, but a reporter must have your consent to use an interview for publication or broadcast. Australian law prohibits recording of calls without consent. Recording phone conversations is legal in all of the 50 states in the USA on certain conditions. Federal law allows recording by a third party as long as one party consents to it. The law is primarily concerned with wire-tapping and law enforcement. This gives reporters a free rein except in a few states such as California, where all parties must consent. [The following sections includes more on recorded interviews and on broadcast telephone interviews.]

Face-to-face interviews

Journalists, both broadcasters and non-broadcasters, prefer face-to-face interviews because they are more personal and help to cultivate contacts. Scheduled interviews may take place in:

Radio or TV studios: The station may provide a car to ensure you are on time.

Your office or consulting room: This has the benefit of being on your territory, usually at a time of your choice.

Neutral territory: Bars or restaurants can be noisy and distracting. Moreover, interviewing can be incompatible with eating and drinking. Almost anywhere quiet and comfortable and devoid of distractions and interruptions will do. Some conference venues have designated interview rooms.

Home: Some press officers warn that interviewees may give away too much of themselves at home. This has to be a personal decision. I prefer home interviews for individual profiles. I am a journalist. I am nosy, but like most journalists, I respect that people may want to draw a dividing line between the personal and professional.

Radio cars: These mini outside broadcast units enable people to be interviewed outside their homes. This is often a strange experience for an interviewee, but it does impress the neighbours when the radio car mast rises high above the street.

Unscheduled media interviews take place at:

Press conferences: See pages 80-81.

Symposia: A reporter at a meeting may want to talk about your presentation – or someone else's. Only you can know if you are prepared. [See Chapter Four: *Preparing for a media interview*.]

"Snatches" or "doorsteps": Classic examples involve reporters and cameramen confronting alleged villains on the doorstep by surprise, but anyone, anywhere, can be "doorstepped", and you need to be circumspect. For example, you could inadvertently disclose embargoed information to a reporter while leaving a meeting. Premature publication of an embargoed story might then scupper further coverage in rival publications. The best defence against a "doorstep" is a simple, prepared response such as: "I'm sorry, but it would be inappropriate for me to say anything before publication of an embargoed report." The more authoritative you sound, the better.

Crisis responses

Prepared crisis responses are essential. "No comment" is almost always inappropriate and, in the event of tragedy, sounds brutal. Explain that further information will become available and apologise if nothing more can be said at that time. When families are bereaved, start by acknowledging their loss. We have all heard interviews beginning: "Our feelings at this time are with the families…" This may sound trite, but anything less sounds heartless.

Third parties

A photographer may accompany a print or website reporter and sit in on the interview, usually unobtrusively, taking dozens of shots. Don't start to fret that this means you are hard to photograph: editors want a wide range of options.

A press or PR officer may also sit in. In *Interviewing for Journalists*, Sally Adams complains that PRs can sour the one-to-one relationship that makes for a good interview.[5] But a press officer may be a reassuring presence and a corrective if you are tempted to say something indiscreet. They may also add details that you may not have to hand.

Recording interviews

This can provide proof of what is said while letting the reporter focus more on listening and encouraging conversational flow. Many reporters take written notes because transcribing speech is extremely time-consuming. Some use recordings as back-up.

Most interviewees soon forget that they are being recorded. An old trick for handling nervous or reticent interviewees is to turn off the recorder, declare the interview over, thank the subject, who usually visibly relaxes, and then to turn the recorder on again for just "one or two more questions" – perhaps the most penetrating. It's good to be relexed but some circumspection may still be required! Regard anything said after the recorder has been turned off as on the record unless there is a specific understanding otherwise. This is true even within the confines of the ladies' or gents' when many people let their guard down. [For more on what is meant by on and off the record, see Chapter Three: *Responding to a media interview request.*]

Additional questions

After the interview the reporter may have supplementary questions. Offering your telephone numbers and email addresses for last-minute questions and checks may prevent errors and help to cultivate an invaluable contact. Many journalists regard it as essential for interviewees to be available on the phone after an interview as there are inevitably times when they want to check something.

Previewing copy

Will you be able to see written copy before publication? Some publications, including national newspapers, have a policy of not showing copy to interviewees in case it compromises the objectivity of journalists. Others, such as celebrity magazines, have all copy checked. Some rely on the individual journalist's judgement. There may, anyway, be insufficient time for previewing.

If you insist on seeing copy before publication, journalists may seek alternative interviewees. Even if you do see the copy you will not usually have the right to withdraw anything you regret saying, or any right to request comments about you from third parties be removed unless you can prove them to be wrong. You may not like what it is or how it is written, but this is the cost of a free press.

Last-minute editing errors may be beyond the reporter's control. For example, I checked a story involving the UK Raynaud's and Scleroderma Association over the phone.[6] Published fully in the first edition of *The Observer,* it was cut in later editions to make room for a late-breaking story. The director, Ann Mawdsley, did not see the first edition and wrote me an angry letter beginning: "It was with great frustration that I read the article on Sunday. We have had phone calls from members asking if we knew about it and, of course, I said not only did we know about it, we gave the information."

She concluded: "All we asked for was the Association to get a mention in return for helping with the article. You said I would be quoted and that also didn't happen. At the end of the day it makes me realise that you can't trust anyone in the media and I find that very sad. Just another story for my book."[7] [And mine!]

I did quote her but I cannot imagine – after so many years in the business – *promising* to do so. Reporters usually lose control of copy when it is passes to editors. Think twice before blaming them for lapses of omission. They will be equally frustrated, and even more so, as frequently happens, if the story is not published at all. [Incidentally, Mawdsley apologised and I apologised on behalf of *The Observer*. We resumed an amicable working relationship.]

What about interviews due to be broadcast? It is rare for an interview to be played back to an interviewee. And again, play-back would not take account of late editing. Cuts are often made as an interview is being broadcast if time is running out. [See also the Live and recorded section later in this chapter.]

Press conferences

Run by commercial companies, governments, professional bodies, universities and charities, press conferences range from massive showcases at international meetings, with hundreds of reporters and cameramen, to small affairs with embarrassingly low turnouts, with more speakers than reporters. High-profile conferences can be nerve-racking, but remember, an invitation to sit on the platform is a vote of confidence in you.

A conference usually begins with statements from speakers, typically two or three. The chairperson then invites questions and asks journalists to identify themselves. How should you pitch answers? British politician Lord [Neil] Kinnock recommended: "Always aim a little bit above their heads because they will reach up: if you aim at their bellies, they will think with their balls."[8] What about conferences including both general reporters and specialist medical or science correspondents? Consult the chairperson about how to proceed. One way is to frame answers as you would for lay people during the press conference, while offering to make yourself available afterwards for more technical questions from specialist journalists.

Concern that a mass of questions at a press conference reflects an inadequate presentation is almost always unfounded. The converse is true. Lots of questions means lots of interest.

Press conferences provide opportunities for both scheduled and impromptu interviews. Reporters may approach you afterwards either to check points or for one-to-one interviews. Be prepared for those who save their most searching questions for post-conference interviews. There are no prizes for journalists who file the same story as their rivals do.

Photo credit: *Viad 1988/Shutterstock.com* Large press conferences still occur at major meetings, but press conferences are less common in the social media age than they were in the 20th century. Reporters now spend more time behind their desks and less in "the field".

Web press conferences enable journalists to log in without leaving their desks, but photographic opportunities are extremely limited, the quality of the video stream may be too low for TV and there is no face-to-face interaction between journalists and interviewees.

Radio interviews

We don't read newspapers or web-based stories or watch TV in the shower or while driving. We do listen to radio. Radio is a background medium reflecting the day's changing mood and tempo. Rush-hour breakfast news is full of short, punchy items. Later output is more expansive. You may get more airtime at 11am than at 7.30am, but far fewer listeners.

Radio is an intimate medium. A BBC training course taught me to treat a radio interview like a conversation with a friend. We were told to talk directly with the audience by referring to "you" and to avoid the impersonal "one", as in "One does feel that…" Radio is also a medium for verbal pictures. It plays on the imagination in a way that TV cannot. To take our earlier example, if you say something is as tall as the Eiffel Tower, a radio audience will form a strong mental picture about the scale of what you're talking about.

Morever, radio is a much better medium than TV for medical messaging, according to Dr Mike Smith, described by the *BMJ* as "the Big Daddy media doc of them all". TV audiences, he complains, are distracted by presenters' attire, while TV slots have become shorter.

What makes a good radio interviewee? As with a telephone interview, there is no visible thinking time. No one can see if you are carefully weighing up an issue. Voice is your sole means of communication. You need to sound lively, interested and to be part entertainer, part informer, part educator; and to adapt tone and style for different topics, different programmes and different stations. A classic approach involves talking about the listeners to obtain their attention, involving them in what you say, and, finally, giving them a plan of action. For example, an interview about a new influenza vaccination might mean:

- Gaining their attention: "This affects you, either because you are at direct risk or because you will have friends and relatives who are at risk. Anybody over 65 will be at increased risk from flu in the next few months. Flu can be debilitating and even deadly."
- Involving them: " Please alert friends and relatives over the age of 65 to the risks."
- Describing the plan of action: vaccination.

Radio interview formats
Live studio interview: Think body language, as with telephone interviews. Listeners will "hear" a smile and a well-timed gesture. Also:
- Sit with your back to the production team, if possible, during a studio interview, to minimise potential distractions.
- Sit up straight, slightly forward, to open up your chest to make breathing easier.
- Look the interviewer in the eye as this will help concentration and make you seem more trustworthy and receptive.
- Restrict notes to a few bullet points.

- During the interview, don't look at notes or, even worse, try to read them word for word. You may sound stilted unless you are a professional performer or actor.
- Use short sentences to make clear points.
- Don't over-embroider answers.
- Make key points quickly in case the interview ends early.
- Try to match the interviewer's energy levels.
- Keep your cool. Losing your temper may make "great radio" at enormous cost to your reputation.
- Earlier I stressed the importance of having two or three messages, but don't say: "I have three things I want to say", in case you forget one. This frequently happens.

Pre-recorded interview: See editorial selection of recorded material in the TV section below.

Radio telephone interview: For a live interview the producer or researcher should call you a few minutes beforehand and invite you to listen in over the phone. This is primarily to ensure that you are there waiting, but it will also give you an opportunity to listen to the tone and pace of the programme. Don't switch on a radio in the same room. It will boomerang down the phone and back on air.

Also see telephone interview section at the start of this chapter.

Down the line: This links an interviewee in a remote studio or radio car with a central studio interviewer. It's a bit like talking into a telephone. Again, as with telephone interviews, if the interview is live, you should be linked up a few minutes beforehand.

Panels: These may include experts with conflicting views debating controversial issues. Ask who else is involved before accepting an invitation. You may not want to debate, for example, with animal rights extremists, but would this leave them unchallenged and your view unheard? Panellists are not selected for reticence. You may have to butt in to make yourself heard, especially if you are down the line and cannot gesture a wish to speak.

Chat shows: Guests may be selected more for storytelling ability and personality than healthcare expertise.

Documentary programmes: These may involve more in-depth interviews. The longer an interview, the more likely it is to be edited.

Starting out: Many professional broadcasters begin as hospital radio volunteers; choosing the music, sustaining an entertaining flow of chat, interviewing patients, operating studio equipment and timing shows. Your local radio station may also be a possible starting place – and more forgiving than a national network.

TV interviews

TV is primarily a medium about pictures and people, whereas radio is more a medium of analysis, ideas and argument. This is, of course, a broad generalisation, but, I believe, a fair one. While good TV performers add to pictures, good radio performers create them. A classic way of presenting a big issue on TV is to focus on its impact on the individual. For example, a story about World Aids Day and the outcome of multi- billion-dollar research may begin with an interview with someone diagnosed HIV-positive 25 years ago when that diagnosis was a likely death sentence.

A typical TV appearance may last from ten seconds to three minutes. Five minutes is a long slot. The interviewer may absorb half of it introducing you and the story and asking questions. For example, in a two-minute-20-second interview on BBC *Breakfast Time,* a haematology director at a children's hospital spoke just 238 words. By way of comparison this paragraph contains 66 words.

He was talking about a 12-year-old boy who had received a blood transfusion from a donor with Creutzfeldt-Jakob disease (CJD). The introduction explained that the boy had haemophilia and that, although he was showing no signs of CJD, the family faced years of uncertainty. The interviewee had to be succinct. This was not a time for pontificating. His main message was that, to date, there had never been a single case of CJD being transmitted by a blood product.

I tell TV interviewees – as well as radio interviewees – to imagine themselves summing up the story to a friend in a sentence. For both TV and radio audiences, the interviewee is in one sense, like a friend – a visitor in the living room. Visitors usually want to be entertained, and to be entertaining, especially if they want to be invited back! Health and medical interviews, of course, are not necessarily entertaining, especially those about topics such as CJD. Good TV and radio interviewees strike the right balance between informing, educating and entertaining.

Who do TV companies invite back as regulars? A film-star face, a great voice and sex appeal count for less than basic competence, reliability and being engaging and a good talker. A charismatic but unpunctual performer is a liability. Availability is also critical. A regular slot with, say, a 5.30am start isn't for everyone. The round trip may take two or three hours, all for a few minutes on screen. This demands real commitment.

Accessibility is critical for one-off interviews. Many potential interviewees do not appear on air because they do not get the necessary clearance in time or because secretaries do not prioritise journalists' calls. These problems call for advanced planning, anticipating interview opportunities and getting the right people in the right place at the right time.

TV interview formats

Live studio interviews: [Also see radio section.] There are few places where you are more conspicious than in a TV studio when the camera is on you. There is no place to hide. It can be a lonely experience, less so if you look at the interviewer not the camera. Also:

- Don't look away halfway through a question. It will seem as if you are not listening or are uncomfortable or shifty.
- The harder the question, the more important eye contact.
- Sit up straight without slouching, slumping, wriggling or fidgeting.
- Perch on the front of the seat and lean slightly forward to look alert and engaged. This may be challenging on a deep sofa.
- Ideally, smile when you are introduced, if it is appropriate. Of course, smiling to order is not easy, especially when you are feeling nervous. The most important thing is to look sincere.

Down-the-line: As with radio, this links an interviewee in a remote studio with a central studio. Using an earplug or speaker the interviewee looks directly at the camera lens but cannot see the interviewer. This can be disconcerting for a novice. Try rehearsing by attaching a drawing of a camera lens to a wall and speaking into it from a nearby chair.

On location: An interview in your clinic, laboratory or office may be disruptive if the camera crew want to rearrange the furniture to capture available daylight or to put you in a particular spot. The idea will be to present you in the best possible way, but it may seem as if your professional world is being turned upside down – not what you want just before facing the camera. An adjacent office, if available, may be better .

An internal location may be better than an external one you cannot control. I can still vividly recall children pulling faces at me while I was doing my first piece to camera in central London. Experienced TV professionals are accustomed to reporting against the background of traffic noise or the gaping curiosity of strangers; you may find such distractions off-putting.

Fly-on-the-wall documentaries

Dr Mark Gabbay, a GP in Manchester in the UK, wrote about his practice's experience of featuring in Channel 4's three-part *Cutting Edge* documentary *The Surgery*, an examination of pressure in general practice. Concern that the "fly-on-the-wall" approach might distort reality, harming both staff and patients, led to prolonged negotiations between the practice and production teams. The TV team regretted the amount of influence they conceded to the practice, but mutually agreed ground rules and consent processes are essential to reconcile inevitable tensions between broadcasting and medical agendas.

Gabbay reported: "We were lucky. The television team had high ethical standards. They sought informed consent from patients and bystanders alike, checking with participants again later, particularly those subsequently included in the final films. The crew was small – a cameraman… and a sound engineer in the room during patient consultations, and an assistant and director secreted in the adjoining examination room…

"Many of the patients seemed to enjoy it, and quite a proportion refused to be involved, which was good as it allowed us to feel more normal with the crew-free breaks during a surgery. We worked at our normal pace – I overran as usual. Some of the resultant material was fairly mundane, but in some cases the story could be followed into a patient's home or cover other contacts with the National Health Service, and it was this that made for the most interesting content of the films. We were asked a few questions about particular patients at the end of surgeries, and at various times gave filmed interviews about topics relevant to the developing story. These required quick thinking, and the academic rigour of needing to justify all statements came in handy.

"When I was filmed doing minor surgery, I could feel the piercing, critical eyes of all those surgical registrars and consultants I had worked for as a callow youth, judging my technique – the sense of triumph when the sebaceous cyst came out with capsule intact was memorable. The experience of driving while being interviewed about a puzzling visit to a new patient – with the cameraman crouched in the passenger foot well, and I inwardly checking that the potential audience of driving instructors and traffic police had no cause for complaint, and that a real policeman wasn't about to pull me over – certainly tuned my reflexes and concentrative powers. So was it worth it? Most politicians would give a limb for the opportunities it gave us to publicise our views – in our case about general practice in the inner cities. I cringed at a lot of it when I first saw the 'rushes', but it was definitely worth it in the end."[9]

Other experiences are not so clear cut. For example, most volunteers in the second series of the BBC's *Junior Doctors: Your Life in Their Hands*, underestimated the stress and time pressures of filming that included retakes, interviews and reactions to clinical events.[10] Thousands of hours of footage were filmed for each hour of broadcast.

This reminds me of a TV documentary in which I introduced six clips from six different London locations. Filming the clips alone took the best part of a day because, for example, street noise from police sirens to car radios kept leaking into shots and equipment kept breaking down. Unforeseen challenges, I was told, were the norm not the exception.

Live or recorded?

Experienced media doctors prefer live interviews because they determine what is broadcast and usually get more air time. In contrast, 15 or so questions and answers in a pre-recorded interview may be whittled down to 15 seconds of airtime. The advantage of a pre-record is that, if it goes wrong, you can do it again, whereas you only get one shot with a live interview. A reporter may decide to pre-record an inexperienced interviewee.

Editorial decisions over what is or isn't broadcast or published highlight a long conflict between journalists and those who do not know the media world. Standard advice to reporters is never to give an undertaking to include or exclude a particular answer or recording because any editing decision may rest higher up the command chain. Some programmes ask interviewees to sign interview consent forms to entitle producers to edit, copy, adapt or translate material as they see fit. They may also state that there is no guarantee that particular interviews will be broadcast. Many interviews are left on the cutting-room floor, to the embarrassment of interviewees who have alerted friends and family to them.

More about "noise"

Alcohol: Avoid drinking before a programme. A drink may appeal if you are nervous, but television can amplify the slightest slurring of your voice. Some producers have tongue-loosening alcohol budgets to provoke "noise" of the most sensational kind. Don't let them make "great television" at your expense.

Dress: A plunging neckline worn by a TV presenter can attract more attention than real news. Presenters and reporters may dress ostentatiously, but the golden rule for specialist guests is to wear something that does not attract attention. I learnt this many years ago from a studio discussion about artificial hearts on ITV's *This Morning*, popularly known as "the Richard and Judy show". My fellow panellists were two specialists from the John Radcliffe Hospital in Oxford, and resident doctor Chris Steele. The researcher asked me to wear something bright. I sported a red jacket and a multi-coloured tie. The Radcliffe specialists and Steele were more appropriately dressed, in conservative suits, for a debate about a controversial life-or-death technology. Without prompting, five friends who saw the show commented on my colourful outfit. The discussion had passed them by.

A casual sweater may fit in with a sofa and coffee table for a breakfast-time chat, but conservative dress is usually best. This means an understated medium-coloured suit, a pastel shirt and a contrasting tie for men; a skirt and top or simple dress with plain neckline and sleeves and mid-range colours for women. Some women experience upper-chest flushing when they become nervous, as many do on television. A low neckline may exacerbate this problem. Ties for men are no longer mandatory.

Fine stripes or check patterns on TV can produce strobing, an irritating visual vibration. Shiny jewellery can cause an annoying flare. Dangling, clanky earrings can also be distracting. Any distractions are critical when the viewer may have only one chance to take in what is said, and perhaps not – as mentioned earlier – in ideal conditions. Audience understanding of TV news programmes is widely reported to be often very poor, even in advanced societies. Even the most simple stories are misunderstood. Unlike newspapers, which have target audiences to generate readers and advertising, TV is more inclined to reach out to everyone.

And so, this chapter ends where it began - with the impact of "noise" on media interviews. We now move to a more black-and-white form of communication that is devoid of "noise", but just as challenging.

SUMMARY

- Research suggests that we make judgements about people within about a tenth of a second, not just about superficial qualities such as attractiveness, but also about trustworthiness and competence.
- Journalists prefer face-to-face interviews because they are more personal and help to cultivate personal contacts, but time constraints mean that most interviews are done on the phone.
- A common error in telephone interviews is to talk too fast.
- TV is primarily a medium about pictures and people. Radio is more a medium of analysis, ideas and argument.
- Make key points succinctly and quickly in broadcast interviews in case they finish early.

- Prepared crisis responses are essential. "No comment" is nearly always inappropriate and in the event of a tragedy will sound heartless and unfeeling.
- Mutually agreed ground rules are essential to reconcile inevitable tensions between TV programme makers and healthcare professionals making fly-on-the-wall documentaries.

NOTES AND REFERENCES

1 Willis J, Todorov A (2006) First impressions: making up your mind after a 100-Ms exposure to a face *Psychological Science* 17 7 592-598

2 Liggett J (1974) *The Human Face* Stein and Day p 271

3 These figures emerged from two studies by Albert Mehrabian, professor emeritus of psychology, UCLA. (http://www.kaaj.com/psych/)

4 Brady J (1977) *The Craft of Interviewing* Vintage

5 Adams S, with Hicks W (2001) *Interviewing for Journalists* p 146 Routledge

6 Illman J (1996) Matthew Corbett gave up Sooty because of Raynaud's *The Observer* Sunday, October 13, 1996

7 Mawdsley A (1996) Letter to Jl. October 17. Anne Mawdsley died in 2014 at the age of 72. Diagnosed with Raynaud's in 1975, she founded the Raynaud's and Scleroderma Association in 1982. She raised more than £10 million for research and was at the forefront of the movement to establish patient and carer groups.

8 Kinnock N (1994) Quoted by Cicely Berry in *Your Voice and How to Use It: The Classic Guide to Speaking with Confidence* Virgin Books p 159-60

9 Gabbay M (1997) The Surgery – an insider's view. Medicine and the media *BMJ* 1314:1491

10 Webster S et al (2012) Doctors on television: analysis of doctors' experiences during filming of a documentary in the workplace *BMJ* 345:e8220

Chapter 7

Writing for the media

Read this chapter to find out about:

IDENTIFYING YOURSELF AS A WRITER

FINDING AND DEVELOPING IDEAS

PITCHING A STORY

INTERVIEW TECHNIQUES AND ETIQUETTE

EDITING YOUR WORDS

Increasing public interest in health has created many more writing opportunities. Healthcare professionals begin with the advantage of knowledge about medicine and health. Working in general practice, obstetrics and gynaecology, paediatrics or psychiatry can be a bonus, but breaking into the market is still hard.

It is essential to know what you want to do. A minority of healthcare-professional news writers develop a passion for interviewing and news reporting, though professional staff writers handle most news. Others have a rare talent for making readers laugh. Some become outspoken columnists in the medical press. Others reflect on medical news in national newspapers, on websites and on radio and TV. Some enjoy the total control over subjects that comes with writing obituaries. Others specialise in reviewing or practice management. Some combine writing for the mainstream media with blogging. Others just blog. [see Chapter Eight: *Social media and blogging.*] Most health-professional writers combine clinical practice with journalism. Some make big financial sacrifices for full-time media careers. A tiny minority become very rich.

Success in one area can expand into others, including books, both non-fiction and, very, very occasionally, fiction. Many doctors, like journalists, dream of writing novels. Few actually do so. Notable exceptions include Sir Arthur Conan Doyle, whose stories about Sherlock Holmes, the world's best-known fictional detective, were a small part of his prodigious output; W Somerset Maugham, who drew on his experience as a medical student to write his first bestseller, *Liza of Lambeth;* and Michael Crichton who wrote *The Andromeda Strain* (1969) while he was a medical student at Harvard. He has sold more than 200 million books, 13 of which were made into films, including *Jurassic Park* (1993), and also created the TV series *ER*. Other notable names include Chekhov, a short-story factory, who described medicine as his lawful wife and literature his mistress – and AJ Cronin, best known for his novel *The Citadel*, about a doctor in a Welsh mining village. Several of his novels were adapted for film, radio and TV.

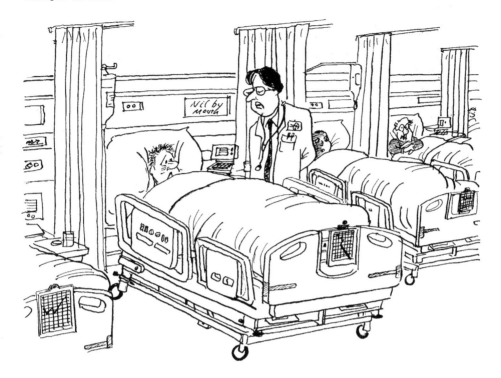

"I can't cure you but I think there may be a novel in it."

Public persona

Part of identifying yourself as a writer is accepting a new kind of public persona that may expose you to the abuse of hate mail. My own Black Library includes a letter to the editor of *The Observer* that reads: "I have never read such a lot of complete b**** before. Your medical correspondent is a total c***. If he had a brain half the size of a peanut, he would know that without medical science there would be no diagnosis or genuine treatment of any disease. This planet would be hell on earth. Sack the silly c*** Illman and the editor who employs him." This followed a mild article about placebo power.

Are healthcare professionals writing on the side as vulnerable as full-time journalists? Probably. For example, Professor Edzard Ernst established the UK's first chair in complementary medicine at the University of Exeter after starting his medical career at Germany's only homeopathic hospital. A prolific media contributor and blogger he is actually an outspoken critic of much complementary medicine. He believes that it should be evidence based and exposed to the same scientific scrutiny as orthodox medicine.

This extract is from an interview we did in 2012:[1]

JI: Do you receive hate mail?

EE: Yes. If I'd been a child molester, some of it couldn't have been more vicious.

JI: Do you keep this hate mail?

EE: Yes. I have many files. My latest book may include some spectacular examples,

JI: To journalists hate mail is often a badge of pride. Is this how you see it?

EE: Yes. It would be very destructive and demoralising if you took it to heart. Collecting it neutralises it.

No one I know has stopped writing because of hate mail. The motives for writing and the desire to write outweigh any anxiety about people who may be more in need of our concern than our contempt. But, as my colleague Tim Albert commented to me, writing is a black and white business. It commits you, and the people you write about, to your statements in a way that speaking does not. Your opinions may be seen to be critical even if you did not intend them to be.[2]

Markets before methods

This section is primarily about writing feature articles as distinct from news. What is a feature article? Broadly speaking, anything that isn't news. Longer than news stories, typically anything between 600 and 2,000 words, features include profiles of people in the news, regular columns, comment pieces, news backgrounders and case histories. A critical lesson in all freelance writing courses is that markets come before methods. Beginners want to know *how to write*. Professional writers think *content* and *audience*, knowing that having these things in clear view will encourage the words to flow. Professionals also know what editors want and how to present it. [Pitching article ideas comes later.]

Developing Ideas

People ask: "What makes a good idea?" I reply: "Tell me something I *don't know. Surprise* me." Ideas are sometimes confused with subjects. For example, cancer screening is a subject. "Cancer screening in some instances could cause more deaths than it prevents" is an idea. Coronary heart disease risk is a subject. "Inflammation could be a bigger cause of heart disease than cholesterol" is an idea. "Good ideas work by challenging preconceptions.

Standard advice is to write about what you know. Better still: write about what readers want to know. Best of all, write about things that readers don't know they need to know until you tell them. Successful people in fields from car design to banking anticipate the future. Aim to do one or more of the following:

- Help readers to see the future.
- Save them money.
- Stop them from making mistakes.
- Help them to do a better job
- Make them laugh.
- Inspire them

Ideally, think of things only you can write about, perhaps being team doctor or physiotherapist or nutritionist to a leading football team or even a really lowly one; or the MO or nurse on a nuclear submarine or cruise liner. Your take on a common experience, such as being a hospital inpatient, may also make compelling copy. Play to your strengths. Very few writers, for example, can make readers laugh.

We are actually surrounded by and exposed to good ideas all the time, but you need to develop the right mindset to recognise them. There may be a gem in a throwaway line by a colleague or a patient; or in an unexpected relevation at a dinner party; or in a conversation with a stranger in a queue – good writers are receptive to ideas.

Idea sources include:

News: This is the biggest single source or "hook" for feature articles. As described in Chapter Two: *The news business*, there are two types of news. "Off the diary" or breaking news stories include the unpredictable such as train crashes, criminal heists and scandals. "Diary" stories include planned events and seasonal happenings such as the start of the new school year and the annual influenza vaccination campaign.

Many feature articles based on diary stories may be written weeks or even months in advance, unlike off-the-diary stories, written immediately. Time between initial production and publication is called "lead time".

Check lead times before submitting ideas to editors – while you may be enjoying late summer, they may be deep into mince pies and Christmas crackers.

Media launches: New books, theatre first nights and radio and TV programmes generate reviews, author profiles and discussion pieces about controversial talking points. Publishers email details of forthcoming book launches and distribute review copies to recognised contributors. How do you become a recognised contributor? Persistence is essential. Google "forthcoming books" or "directory of medical book publishers" for forthcoming titles. Select a title. Email a journal editor offering a review, explaining why you should do it. If your proposal is accepted, email the publisher to request a pre-publication review copy, copying in the journal editor's email as proof of commission. Again, let me stress the need to persist. Don't be disappointed by initial rejection. Becoming an Amazon book reviewer – anyone can do this – may provide evidence of your writing ability and develop your writing skills.

Anniversary features: These mark historical events and developments – from wars to artistic movements. Most countries have anniversary websites such as the ITN Source website in the UK. The 50th anniversary in 2017 of the first human-to-human heart transplant will be a prominent feature in many forward planning diaries.

Press releases: Many features are based on press or news releases. As noted earlier a press or video release is a written or recorded communication distributed to the media to announce something allegedly newsworthy. Releases typically run to about two sides of A4-sized paper. For examples of press releases, visit websites of charities, corporations, government agencies, medical centres, professional and representative bodies and journals; or log on to distribution agencies such as EurekAlert!, PR Newswire or BusinessWire. Specialising in scientific research, EurekAlert! is run by the American Association for the Advancement of Science.

Press releases are distributed either for immediate release or under embargoes that restrict publication until a specific date and time, usually up to several days. Access to embargoed press releases is usually restricted to accredited reporters to give them more preparatory time. See *Embargoed*

Science by Vincent Kiernan[3] for more about the controversial embargo system.

There has been a lively debate about the future of the press release. While tweets, infographics and videos are now seen as more relevant ways of disseminating information, "reports of the death of the press release have been greatly exaggerated", *PR Week* proclaimed in October 2013. The media are still inundated with them.

From idea to completed article

Submit an outline proposal rather than an entire unsolicited article. Someone else may have already written something similar, and unsolicited pieces rarely make it into print. As health editor on *The Guardian* and as editor of *GP*, I received thousands of them. I did not use more than five to ten per cent and did not read beyond the first two paragraphs of most of them. This might sound unkind, but how do consumers treat the media? We actually read very little. We scan a lot. If we don't find something new or different we move on. Editors are the same – to reiterate, they want to be surprised.

GP Dr Carol Cooper, who writes for *The Sun*, Britain's biggest-selling tabloid advises trying to grab the reader's attention in ten words – or even as few as three.[4] This is as true of pitches as finished articles and as true of *The New York Times* as *The Times* of London and the bright and breezy *Sun*. [See Chapter One: *Journalists* for more about Cooper.]

Many aspiring writers follow the IMRAD structure proposed by Sir Austin Bradford Hill, the British epidemiologist and statistician best known for his work with Sir Richard Doll linking smoking and lung cancer. [5] An acronym for Introduction, Materials [and Methods] and Discussion, IMRAD works well for papers in scientific journals, but not for much else. Introductions written in the scientific tradition tend to cover old ground.

Pitching

A pitch should be no more than 200 to 250 words, the shorter the better, with a brief headline such as "Treating the Winter Blues". It should explain:

- What it's about
- What's new about it

- Why now
- How it will affect readers
- Why you. You may have lots of experience treating a condition you are writing about. You may be a patient yourself.
- Who, if anybody, you are interviewing. Quotes can be as important in journalism as scientific evidence is in evaluating treatments. They inject life into text.

Some pitches unfold through character not concept. For example, "John Major used to have irregular, backward-sloping teeth. He now has straight, even, white ones. The former British Prime Minister is not alone. More and more Britons are opting for cosmetic dentistry." Scientists shy away from this kind of anecdotal approach for fear of imbalance, but good journalism blends objective science with subjective experience. [This theme is explored in Chapter Ten: *Media case histories.*]

Most editors prefer email pitches, but a phone call may work – if you can get through and it doesn't happen to be a frantic press day. Try following up an email with a call if you don't get a prompt response to a time-sensitive idea so you can try it elsewhere. Again, perseverance is essential: editors have hundreds of emails in their inboxes at any one time. Emailing an editor can be a bit like sending a message in a bottle and not knowing if it has been read.

It may not matter how good your article is if it lacks an accompanying, eye-catching picture or graphic.

Don't expect feedback about rejections.

Don't be over-ambitious initially. Company newsletters, university magazines, local newspapers and smaller healthcare journals may be better targets than big newspapers such as *The New York Times* and journals such as the *BMJ* and *The Lancet*.

Check the facts
Professional journalists are criticised for inaccuracies. How do clinician writers fare? A Canadian study found that information dispensed in medical advice columns by doctors was often inappropriate and sometimes

dangerous.[6] Dr Frank Molnar, of the division of geriatric medicine at
Ottawa Hospital's civic campus, and his colleagues found that the content
of half of 50 advice columns for elderly people, randomly selected from 109
Canadian English-language columns, was unsuitable for a geriatric patient
population, and in 28 per cent of cases, potentially life threatening.

Five geriatricians rated 50 randomly selected articles from 11 daily
newspaper columns in 1995, on the basis of whether advice, if taken by
intended readers, posed no threat of morbidity [safe]; had some potential
for morbidity but not mortality [unsafe]; or had potentially life-threatening
complications [dangerous]. The reviewers concluded that critical issues
were not clearly identified in 11 columns [22%]; that opinion was likely
to be interpreted as fact in seven [14%]; and that readers would probably
misunderstand for whom the advice was intended in four [8%].

These findings should be seen in context. First, patients may have been
unable to follow the columnists' advice without seeing a doctor. Second,
the columns may have alerted patients to seek medical advice. Third,
as the Canadian authors pointed out, it is hard to be both brief and
comprehensive. This is the biggest challenge of journalism.

Are these findings representative? Even though studies show that
patients get most of their health advice from the media,[7] this is an under-
researched area. A British GP and author, the late Dr Ann McPherson,
called for a review of medical advice columns after monitoring doctor
columnists in national newspapers.[8]

Asked how well radiotherapy worked in breast cancer, one columnist
replied that it was an effective form of treatment fairly well tolerated by
most patients. This was an inadequate answer, McPherson ruled, because
while radiotherapy stopped local recurrence, it did not stop cancer
spreading elsewhere and did not affect five-year mortality. Another
columnist, she complained, had made an assertion seem true by use of
numbers without citing supporting evidence.

McPherson's suggestion that health articles "just need some time and
research" may seem trite and obvious, but my own editing experience
suggests that some doctors rely on out-of-date knowledge. What are the

criteria for success? DISCERN was developed in the UK as a means of judging the quality of consumer health information on treatment choices. It says that information about treatment choices for consumers should:

- Have explicit aims
- Achieve its aims
- Be relevant
- Make sources of information explicit
- Make date of information explicit
- Be balanced and unbiased
- List additional sources of information
- Refer to areas of uncertainty
- Explain how treatment works
- Describe treatment benefits
- Describe treatment risks
- Say what would happen without treatment
- Explain effects of treatment choices on overall quality of life
- Make it clear there may be more than one treatment choice
- Provide support for shared decision-making.

See discern.org.uk for the full Discern instrument and additional advice.

As mentioned in Chapter One: *Journalists,* in 2006 Gary Schwitzer, a former CNN medical correspondent, launched healthnewsreview.org, which evaluates US news stories that make therapeutic claims about investigational drugs or devices, vitamins or nutritional supplements, diagnostic and screening tests, dietary recommendations and surgical procedures. Using a standardised rating system, a multi-disciplinary team of reviewers from journalism, medicine, health service research and public health assess stories in leading newspapers, broadcast stations, websites and news agencies such as Reuters Health and Associated Press. See healthnewsreview.org for critiques of graded stories.

Reviewers seek answers in news stories to these questions:
- What's the total cost?
- How often do benefits occur?
- How often do harms occur?
- How strong is the evidence?

- Is the condition exaggerated?
- Are there alternative options?
- Is it really a new approach?
- Is it available to me?
- Who's promoting this? Do they have a conflict of interest?
- Does the story rely solely or largely on a press [news] release?

This last point is important. If you think of basing an article on a press release, remember that the organisations that issue them have vested interests, possibly commercial. In 2015 Schwitzer and his team began systematically reviewing press releases from government agencies, medical journals, academic medical centres and commercial companies. For example, a press release from King's College, London, suggesting that cognitive behaviour therapy could replace sedation for dental phobias was awarded three stars out of a possible five by the team for its "somewhat useful findings". A report on how the food industry could make junk food more healthy by adding seaweed merited only two stars and was deemed dubious.

Interviewing
It helps an interviewer to know the demands of being an interviewee. Chapters Three to Six cover responding to media interview requests and preparing for and giving interviews.

Selecting interviewees: These may include other healthcare professionals and patients. Good interviewees speak in plain language, get to the point quickly and tell engaging stories. They don't sound as if they are dictating a paper for a scientific journal and don't talk about such things as hazard ratios and forest plots, unless the interview is for a statistical or scientific journal.

Don't be put off if an interviewee initially turns you down. Most people are modest or like to appear so and may be nervous about speaking in public. This is especially true of researchers and bench-based scientists who have been encouraged to keep their heads below the media parapet. They may be waiting for you to ask again – seeking what I call a "permission card'. Most of us like talking about things we know about. In my experience about 95 per cent of people will agree to a media interview, but some need a little time to think about it.

Many patients like to talk about their treatment, seeing it as a way of helping others, or as a means of thanking healthcare professionals, or as a cathartic experience. Patient interviewees are discussed in Chapter Ten: *Media case histories*.

I have already referred to the similarities between medical consultations and media interviews. For example, proficient healthcare professionals and journalists routinely ask both open questions and closed ones [requiring the answer yes or no], watch for giveaway facial expressions and show understanding and empathy. They are also good listeners and know the value of silence – and how it is ultimately filled.

Similarly, doctors/journalists conducting consultations/interviews may reach premature conclusions about a possible diagnosis or a story angle that may blind them to other possibilities. Standard advice is to be clear before starting an interview about what you want to achieve. This is good advice for an interviewee: bad advice for an interviewer. Why do an interview if you already know what you want to achieve? A good interview explores the unknown. One of artist Richard Diebenkorn's ten rules on beginning a painting also applies to interviewing: "Do search. But in order to find other than what is searched for."

Building on the unexpected is a challenge. As in a consultation, it is easy to miss a flashpoint – a moment when, perhaps in just a few words, the interviewee frames an interview, making it really exciting and *surprising* [that word again]. This is less likely to happen with an "interviewing by numbers" approach – working your way through a prepared list of questions without hesitation or deviation. I may ask no more than four or five out of 15 to 20 prepared questions. Preparing a long list of questions is nonetheless invaluable, acquainting you with your interviewee and their expertise.

Dress: This is no time for a fashion statement. Quiet is better than loud. Focus on drawing the interviewee out, not drawing attention to your amusing tie or flamboyant suit.

Introducing yourself: It will help your interviewee to know how much you know about their specialist subject and about the extent of your journalistic experience. Keep it simple and succinct. The interview is not about you.

Rules of engagement: Sum up in about 15 seconds how you see the story and what you want to cover. Check how much time they have. Have they any questions before you begin? Do they mind if you record the interview? If that's the plan, it is polite to ask. What happens if they want to go off the record? [See Chapter Three: *Responding to a media interview request.*]

Notebook or recorder? Transcribing recorded interviews can take hours. A notebook is the easiest and quickest option, especially if you have immaculate shorthand, but recording face-to-face interviews lets you concentrate on and maintain eye contact with the interviewee and provides incontrovertible evidence of what has been said. Turn off the recorder as soon as possible after an interview and jot down the key points. These will almost certainly be the most critical. Material you cannot easily recall will probably be unimportant. Check selected material, especially direct quotations, with the recorder.

A word of warning: do not get so carried away by the conversation that you talk over your interviewee and go home to transcribe your own immortal opinions.

At the end: Thank the interviewee and ask:
- If there is anything they'd like to add
- If there are any questions you should have asked, but didn't
- If there is anyone else you should talk to
- If you can contact them again if, necessary, to check additional points, perhaps by email.

Previewing copy: As discussed in the preceding chapter, the interviewee may ask to see what you have written before publication. This can create complications. For example, the copy may be edited after it has left your hands, or the interviewee may want to edit or rewrite it, perhaps in a wholly inappropriate way. A good compromise may be a telephone check in which you read the text.

I was trained not to show copy to interviewees, partly because, in the pre-internet era, it was time-consuming and incompatible with deadlines. Moreover, the original copy might have been edited, cut or reworded by a senior editor or sub-editor – this is still the case. But now, if I have a good rapport with interviewees, I will email them copy. This can produce additional, invaluable material and cultivate contacts. So, there are no hard and fast rules. Use your discretion unless your editor expressly forbids "copy approval" in any form, as some do.

Style

The English writer Matthew Arnold said: "Have something to say, and say it as clearly as you can. That is the only secret of style." George Orwell's six rules of style endorse this advice:

- Never use a metaphor, simile or other figure of speech you are used to seeing in print
- Never use a long word where a short one will do
- If it is possible to cut out a word, cut it out
- Never use the passive where you can use the active
- Never use a foreign word, a scientific word or a jargon word if you can think of an everyday English equivalent
- Break any of these rules sooner than say anything outright barbarous.

Examples of long words and better shorter ones include:
- Additional – extra
- Administer – give
- Adopt – use
- Advocate – support
- Ameliorate – improve
- Commence – begin
- Complete – finish
- Constructed – made
- Consulted – asked
- Demonstrate – show
- Exists – is
- Prior to – before
- Purchase – buy

There are exceptions to Orwell's pruning advice. For example, Abraham Lincoln began one of the most famous speeches in US history, the Gettysburg Address,[9] with, "Four score and seven years ago". He may have been the first man in history to use the phrase. Starting this stirring speech about American destiny with "Eighty-seven years ago" would have lacked the same ring of history and authority. Despite his fleeting deviation from Orwell's Law, Lincoln's brevity would have impressed the novelist. His 272-word address took just over two minutes.

House style

When should you use single or double quotes? Or hyphens? All publications have house styles to ensure consistency of spellings, abbreviations, proper names, punctuation and technical terms and to discourage careless, trite or boring language. Contributors who ignore house style irritate editors. There is no point in writing in the style of a mass circulation tabloid such as *The Sun* for *The New York Times*.

"This prescription is pretty dull. Could you rewrite it in the style of a Daily Express headline."

The Associated Press Stylebook and Briefing on Media Law, known as the AP Stylebook, is accepted in the US as a general guide, and includes an A-Z listing covering abbreviation, capitalisation, number use, spelling and word usage. I also recommend *The Oxford Dictionary for Writers and Editors* and *Guardian Style*.

Checking copy

Most people seem to find it harder to pick up errors on a computer screen than on the printed page, but on-screen checking is routine now that we use printers less and work remotely, possibly without printer access. My editor Rose Shepherd commented: "Reading from a screen is undoubtedly slower and blanket reading more difficult. We read better when we are looking down on the page, otherwise we'd all hold up books in front of our faces."

If possible, ask someone else to check your copy and:
- Save a copy before reading it in case you make changes that have to be undone.
- Run the spell/grammar check. Double check for mistypes that the spell check won't pick up, such as casual and causal. Watch out for homophones, words that sound the same or similar but have different meanings and spellings – there/their, to/too, know/no, here/hear, accept/except, bare/bear, fair/fare, principle/principal, compliment/ complement. Words are also commonly misused. For example, 'farrago' instead of 'fiasco', and 'flaunt' instead of 'flout'. Use a dictionary to avoid these malapropisms.
- Magnify the page to 200 per cent or whatever size suits
- Check a line at a time by highlighting it in a contrasting colour
- Check the ends of sentences that run onto the next line
- Limit checking to 20-minute sessions
- Divide checking into areas, beginning with spelling mistakes and grammar, then punctuation and house style and so on
- Read the text out loud to identify errors and clumsy language. Yes, this really works
- Finally, try a backwards read, on paper, starting at the foot. It is amazing what jumps out at you when you don't read for sense because you can't.

The Coolidge lesson

The most common reason for failing as a writer is giving up. People assume they "cannot write" if the words don't flow. This reminds me of the framed quotation by US President Calvin Coolidge on my office wall: "Nothing in the world can take the place of persistence. Talent will not; nothing is more common than unsuccessful men with talent." This reassures me when the going gets tough and lonely – as it inevitably does.

Blogging

Writing a blog will help you to develop your writing. Success in the field will establish your reputation and may lead to invitations to contribute to newspapers, journals and radio and TV. The next chapter describes how to start a blog and includes more on developing ideas. Please read it in tandem with this one.

SUMMARY

- Markets before methods. Beginners want to know how to write. Professional writers think content and audience.
- Standard advice: write about what you know. Better still: write about what readers want to know. Best of all, write about things they don't know they need to know until you tell them.
- Successful articles do one or more of the following: help readers to see the future; save them money; stop them from making mistakes; help them to be better at what they do; inform them; make them laugh.
- Pitch ideas rather than sending complete articles. Someone else may have submitted something similar.
- An accompanying eye catching picture or graphic may make the difference between an article idea being accepted or rejected.
- When it comes to style, keep it simple.

NOTES AND REFERENCES

1   Illman J (2012) Interview. Edzard Ernst. *HealthWatch newsletter* No 87. October

2   Albert T (1992) *Medical Journalism. The Writer's Guide* p7 Radcliffe Medical Press

3   Kiernan V (2006) *Embargoed Science* University of Illinois Press

4   Cooper C (2002) *A Guide to Medical Publishing and Writing* Edited by Peter Richardson p76 Quay Books. Mark Allen Publishing. p76 [Dr Cooper was one of a number of contributors.]

5   Bradford Hill A. Developed in the 1960s.

6   Molnar FJ et al (1999) Assessing the quality of newspaper medical advice columns for elderly readers *Canadian Medical Association* Journal 161 393-5

7   McPherson A (1999) The problem with medical advice columns *BMJ* 319 928

8   Ibid

9   Lincoln A (1863) Lincoln delivered the Gettysburg Address during the American Civil War to reiterate the principles of human equality laid down in the Declaration of Independence.

Chapter 8

Social media and blogging

Read this chapter to find out about:

SOCIAL MEDIA AS A WRITING AND
COMMUNICATIONS PLATFORM

STARTING A BLOG

GENERATING BLOG IDEAS

TWEETING

RISKS AND PITFALLS

Social media extend the most important thing we do every day – talking to one another. Think of this as digital word of mouth: a new means of campaigning, challenging, commentating, connecting, engaging, entertaining, informing, influencing, inspiring, leading, learning, motivating, persuading, reflecting, sharing and supporting. For example:

Campaigning

Diagnosed with cancer aged 29, and dismayed by doctors and nurses who did not introduce themselves, Dr Kate Granger, a UK elderly medicine specialist, launched the "hello-my-name-is" campaign in 2013. She explained: "I have always been a strong believer in getting to know people's names as part of building good working relationships with both patients and colleagues. I think it is the first rung on the ladder to providing compassionate care, and often getting the simple things right first means the more complex things will follow more easily and naturally."[1]

The then Secretary of State for Health Jeremy Hunt and then Prime Minister David Cameron commended her and thousands of clinical staff have made online pledges to introduce themselves to patients. Many hospital wards display staff names and pictures on #hellomynameis boards. NHS England with NHS Employers recognised her work in 2014 with the inauguration of the annual Kate Granger Awards for Compassionate Care.

The campaign was built up around Granger's Twitter feed and blog. For the uninitiated, Twitter is an online messaging service restricted [at the time of writing] to 140 characters per message or "tweet". A blog is a regularly updated website or webpage. Called "posts", updates are typically displayed in reverse chronological order, the most recent appearing first. Posts can include pictures and links to videos and other websites. The campaign worked because of:

- Simplicity of the message.
- The brush-fire-like power of social media. Tweets that resonate with an audience are retweeted, sometimes to many thousands of people.
- Its impact on healthcare professionals. [Were they *really* failing to do something as basic and simple as introducing themselves to patients?]
- Minimal financial cost
- Granger's engaging personality and powerful story.

Granger said in 2014: "What has struck me since I began to publicly share my experience nearly two years ago is just how powerful the voice of a clinician living on the other side can be. I never dreamed anyone would listen to what I had to say, but now my voice has been heard I am determined to use it in the most positive way possible in my remaining time."[2]

Photo credit: *Reproduced by kind permission of Dr Kate Granger.*
Granger's Twitter page. She joined Twitter in 2012 and quickly built up tens of thousands of followers in her campaign to encourage healthcare professionals to introduce themselves to patients. Note how the foreground picture on the left highlights eye contact, one of the most immediate and powerful forms of human communication. The image signposts the background picture of supporters of the "hello-my-name-is" campaign. A similar picture below, from 2015, shows the campaign attracting continuing support.

Informal but authoritative, her writing strikes an ideal balance for social media. Highlighting a compassionate and feeling doctor, it makes her own negative experience as a terminal cancer patient all the more disturbing. Her output includes two books, *The Bright Side* and *The Other Side*. The latter was written to help healthcare professionals understand what it is really like to be a patient and how they affect patients.[3]

Her blog, however, is not a "professional only" site. Followers include fellow patients and their friends and relatives. Healthcare professionals and patients are joining forces in ways that used to be unthinkable, and sharing more and more information, much of it personal. The possible negative consequences of blurring personal and professional relationships online are discussed later.

Reflecting

Inspired by Granger, Dr Elin Roddy, a respiratory specialist, became a lead for end-of-life care after provoking a Twitter "storm" with Dying Matters, a moving blog about care of the dying and their loved ones. She wrote that this was one of the most important jobs healthcare professionals could do and something that they should value more highly. Roddy is a classic example of someone who has resonated with a social media audience through thought-provoking content. Her Twitter followers include healthcare professionals, patients, carers, the bereaved – and, we may be sure, journalists. Now part of a national debate she could become a valuable contact for journalists writing about care of the dying, especially if, for example, she spoke out for/against euthanasia.

Educating

"Wrongfooted" is a blog post about an operation on the wrong foot, showing the power of social media to disseminate critical safety messages to large audiences.[4] Viewed 5,000 times within 24 hours and posted by anaesthetist Dr Helgi Johannsson, then at Imperial College London, it begins, significantly, with a vote of thanks to the authority's medical director for giving Johannsson permission to talk openly about what went wrong. This extended the scope of learning way beyond just one hospital – to the whole world.

What did go wrong? The anaesthetist saw the patient before the operation, but didn't check which leg was to be operated on. The anaesthetic nurse noted that the patient lacked a stocking for the leg not being operated on, and asked the ward nurse for one. The patient put the stocking on the wrong leg. The anaesthetic nurse read out the WHO checklist. The surgeon was listening but was scrubbing up in a side room. The nurse in charge was on the phone. The second scrub nurse was upstairs getting equipment. The anaesthetist was getting the patient settled on the ventilator…

Fortunately the patient was due to have surgery on both feet and made an uneventful recovery, but the operation had a devastating effect on staff. Johannsson, however, saw the incident as a "fantastic opportunity to demonstrate how safety works". Limiting telling what happened to within the hospital, he said, would have been an enormous disservice to patients.

Blogging about a similar error elsewhere, surgeon Dermot O'Riordan said that his team had adopted a transparent and open approach, but he regretted not sharing their learning as Wrongfooted had done. He had feared that this might invite journalistic interest. There were also patient and staff confidentiality concerns. His anxiety was understandable, but deliberate intent to keep the episode out of the public domain could actually have made a bigger media story than the event itself.

Johansson and Wrongfooted did actually make headlines – but not of the kind O'Riordan feared. Johannsson was named in 2012, along with Kate Granger, by *HSJ (Health Service Journal)* and *Nursing Times*, as one of 12 social media pioneers by a team of judges made up of the very people O'Riordan feared – journalists.[5]

Increasing awareness

Two other of the *HSJ/Nursing Times* pioneers are nurse Sally-Ann Marciano and intensivist Dr Ron Daniels. Marciano works to create awareness about the need for better dementia care. Her father had Alzheimer's disease. A passionate advocate of using social media to advance professional development, she has nearly 7,000 Twitter followers at the time of writing. One of the first of its kind, her blog described her father's acute hospital care, end-of-life care at home and concern that no one was responsible for coordinating his care. She runs an influential online learning network and has worked on a government task force.

Daniels aims to increase awareness of sepsis. A committed blogger and chief executive of the UK Sepsis Trust website, he developed the concept of Sepsis Six to improve basic care after watching a 37-year-old man die from the condition in 2005. The website includes information for patients and healthcare professionals, a news section and case histories.

Debating

Dr Kevin Pho, a US internal medicine physician in New Hampshire and co-author of a social media guide for physicians,[6] publishes guest posts on his blog KevinMD.com by fellow healthcare professionals, medical students and lawyers. He recalls how a plaintiff attorney's post on medical malpractice provoked "a firestorm of comment" not only from doctors, but also from other lawyers and injured patients. One patient commented that KevinMD.com was the only internet site where doctors, lawyers and patients could unite to debate controversial topics such as medical malpractice in a relatively civilised and constructive way. More than 2,000 authors have contributed to his site since he founded it in 2004. It is frequently cited in mainstream media, from the *Wall Street Journal* to CNN to *The New York Times* which described his blog as a "highly coveted publishing place for doctors and patients".

Social media, Pho realised, offered a powerful forum for debate. Should such debate be restricted to professional-only sites? Pho maintains that it is acceptable to engage with patients collectively, but not individually, on social networks. [You can send either private messages to individuals or general messages to all your followers on social networks such as Twitter.]

Social media platforms

These include:

Twitter This is now so ingrained in public consciousness that it is hard to believe that it was only founded in 2006. By March 2015, it had more than 600 million users, of whom 289 million were active.[7] It is the internet's principal news and information service.

Facebook With more than 1.4 billion active accounts [March 2015], Facebook is the Internet's cocktail party and a place to interact with friends and family and swap pictures of weddings, graduation ceremonies and newborns.[8] It does have a more cerebral side, with communities for writers including Where Writers and Authors Meet and The Creative and Professional Writing Information Exchange.

Google-plus was reported in February 2014 to have 1.5 billion users, yet was dubbed a "ghost town" because only 35 per cent of its users were active. It provides a forum for promoting ideas and sharing information, experience and knowledge. It is highly recommended for writers because of its powerful search-engine optimisation (SEO) capacity. Effective SEO results in a higher search engine ranking, which will drive traffic to your website. There is more about SEO later in this chapter. Google Plus also has writers' communities, including Writing Resources and the Writer's Discussion Group.

LinkedIn By the third quarter 2014, LinkedIn had 332 million users. It is an online résumé or CV directory with links to editors, publishers and agents.[9]

YouTube has more than a billion users a month and is a free video- sharing website. Unregistered users may watch videos. Registered users can upload an unlimited number of them.

Many internet platforms are linked so that, for example, a user can automatically update a Facebook profile from a Twitter account. There is more later in this chapter about how this can blur the boundary between personal and professional activity.[10] These platforms can also be linked to blogs.

Creating and writing a blog

As noted earlier a blog is a website or webpage that is regularly updated with posts [contributions]. Before you start your own, study state-of-the art blogs such as Scepticemia, Musings of a Skeptic Oslerphile; Wing of Zock [the name comes from the bestselling novel *House of God*, about the life of a group of interns in a US teaching hospital]; Less is More Medicine; and Dr. Wes.[11] Note how these sites combine text, images and links to other blogs and web pages and invite comments from readers.

Each of them is unique, though much of what they say is not. Writing for physicians about everything from income to the decision to invite Hillary Clinton to speak at a medical conference, Dr. Wes scores by being controversial and outspoken. He does not have a so-called USP [unique selling proposition], more an ESP [emotional selling proposition].

The evidence-based Less is More Medicine examines such topics as screening, healthcare costs, patient perspective, overdiagnosis, over-testing and over-treating. These are widely debated issues, but Less is More has a distinct identity and is driven by the conviction of the founder, Dr Jessica Otte, a Vancouver-based family physician, that: "By doing less of the unnecessary stuff, we can do more of the right stuff."

Kate Granger has a USP and an ESP that shine through her writing. For example, her post, Dear Cancer, on July 29, 2014, is a witty note to her own cancer to mark their three-year "cancerversary". It begins: "Usually I would start penning a letter to someone significant with 'how are you?' or perhaps 'hope this finds you well', but both these conversational niceties seem wholly inappropriate when writing to you. I certainly don't want to know how you are doing and I certainly don't want to encourage your well-being. It has now been three years to the day since we kicked off this unusual relationship of ours and I figured I should mark this latest and unexpected cancerversary by recording some feelings and reflections."

Setting up

Log onto a hosting site such as blogger.com or wordpress.com or tumblr. com on an independent website with a so-called blog feed that will post material onto the internet. Hosting sites are usually free, but you may wish to pay for additional services – for example, if you wish to a run a shop from your site. Independent websites may cost between $5,000 and $25,000 or more to build and maintain.

Naming your blog

This is critical – the name is the first thing seen on internet search engines. The memorable names above feature high in the top listings of major search engines. For example, try searching for Dr. Wes. When I googled him, his site appeared at the top of the first page. Imagine that you want to blog about critical care. Calling it "Critical Care" wouldn't work because a Google search of "critical care blogs" [December 2015] produced 85,800,000 results. Although the name Dr. Wes may mean little to the world at large, there is, I believe, only one Dr. Wes online and only one with a blog about "Musings in the life of an internist, cardiologist and cardiac electrophysiologist".

Avoid online pseudonyms. The Royal College of General Practitioners (RCGP) reported that some healthcare professionals had wrongly believed that pen names would protect them from disciplinary action for unprofessional behaviour. Posts may last for ever, the RCGP pointed out, but online anonymity may be temporary.[12] Don't post anything you wouldn't be prepared to say on live TV. It is relatively easy in many countries to get a court order against a website host or even Twitter to identify the author of an anonymous post.[13]

There is another consideration. Publishing under your own name will help to build that most precious of things, your professional reputation – anonymity will not.

Choosing post titles

The title, the only initially visible bit of a post, determines whether or not it is read. A title should do one or more of these things:

Stress a benefit. For example:
- Making the most of your waiting room
- Operating as a sole trader
- Boosting practice income.

Create controversy. For example:
- Neck-vein surgery for MS – breakthrough or false hope?
- Clinical trials: why I blew the whistle
- Statins fail to reduce risk of death.

Ask a question. For example:
- When is a procedure cosmetic?
- Ebola: an opportunity for a clinical trial?
- Should marijuana be legal?

Include "you" in the title: For example:

- Suspected breast cancer: when should you refer?
- What will you earn as a junior doctor?
- Helping you to become a cardiologist.

As already noted "you" is reported to be the most effective word in advertising. It is personal and reaches out to us.

So-called listicles also attract readership. A listicle is list-based article.[14] For example, *Ten things GPs need to know about pharmacists.* [15]

Some titles/headlines defy journalistic convention. For example, upworthy.com has been commended for curating the best of social media, but attacked for its "curiosity gap" titles. They have little or nothing to do with the text, but tease the reader into clicking onto them. A video about US healthcare was entitled: *His First 4 Sentences Are Interesting. The 5th Blew My Mind and Made Me a Little Sick.* This may not be for you, but Upworthy must be doing something right. Focusing on social issues for young audiences, its 100 most popular posts were viewed and shared more than 380 million times in 2013, while its record monthly visitor figure topped 87 million, similar to that of *The Guardian*. Highly acclaimed for its online content, this London newspaper is nearly 200 years old,[16] while Upworthy was only launched in 2012. I stand by my advice that a title should convey a benefit, but the ultimate test is whether or not it makes the reader click on it — and stay on it.

Search engine optimisation (SEO)

What makes the reader click? It is not enough to write brilliant posts. SEO is the key to a high ranking in search engines such as Google and Yahoo. The higher your ranking, the more visitors your blog or website will attract. How does it work? SEO will unite you with your target audience on the basis of key words in your blog posts.

For example, imagine you had written a blog post about "junior doctor earnings". These would become key words in your post. The best key words are two to four-word phrases that sum up what a particular piece of content is about. Why two to four words? Because we commonly use phrases of this length in internet searches. The more unusual your key words, the better. If I were to write a blog post containing the key words "King Munchausen

Rides Again" and you were to tap the very same words into the Google search bar, you would almost certainly, thanks to SEO, be directed straight to my post. But what would happen if your key words were restricted to "junior doctor earnings"? A Google search has just identified more than 200,000 sites featuring junior doctor earnings. Fortunately, there are other ways to alert target audiences to your blog posts. You could tweet a link to your followers. [There is more about tweeting later in this chapter.] Better still, build a loyal following that will visit your site without prompting.

Blogging style and writing

Blogs have shaken up and extended medical and science writing. They reflect a broad spectrum of writing styles, from the academic and scientific to, more commonly, the informal and approachable. UK psychology blogger Dave Munger, of Research Blogging, advises newcomers to put something of themselves into their blogs. He says that doesn't mean sharing all your deepest secrets, but that indicating who you are and why you love psychology is the quickest way to link an audience."[17]

The same is true of other disciplines. All the bloggers cited in this chapter inject a lot of themselves into their writing. Ron Daniels, for example, started with: "This blog will be my own account of the last 8 years of my professional life – I'll aim to highlight errors I've learned from, ideas that have brought success, and inspire others to work from the shop floor to affect patient-focused change. There have been times of enormous self-doubt and challenge along the way, but it has been worth it. The blog is likely to expose the real Ron – the sometimes introspective, self-critical, but passionate and determined 'me', and I sincerely hope you'll bear with me on this."[18]

Thirty years ago physicians would not have adopted this style in a public forum, but what is wrong, as GP Margaret McCartney noted, with admitting to fallibility and a human side if you respect professional boundaries and endorse good care?[19]

As a writer, you may begin while not knowing exactly how to get to where you want to go. For example, you may have a clear message, like Kate Granger's "My name is", but be unclear about how to say it. Writing is often an experiment, and never more so than now. Had I been a doctor writing in the pre-internet era, I would have presented only the professional me, the detached me. I'd have been constrained by demands of editors and the minutiae of journal house style. Now, within just a few minutes, I could decide my own house style and how to present myself to the online world – all without training, guiding precedents, the restraining hand of colleagues and an editor… The same is true of you. Within a few clicks you could be a published author. Scary!

The novice's dilemma

As structural biologist and blogger Professor Stephen Curry, director of undergraduate studies at Imperial College, London, noted: "Starting a blog may be technically straightforward – all you need do is to log on and start typing – but for a scientist who has only previously published research papers, the immediacy of blog writing feels strange, even dangerous. There is not the protection of peer review by colleagues who will catch your more egregious errors before publication."[20]

He is one of a new generation of scientists and healthcare professionals that, as it has grown in expertise and stature, has surprised itself, I believe, by reaching out to external audiences. For example, Curry recalled: "Before long I found myself banging on the door of *The Guardian* demanding – and getting – right of reply to Simon Jenkins [a former editor of *The Times* in London] who, riffing off the non-appearance of a bird flu epidemic, had castigated scientists as a self-considered clerisy that regarded itself above criticism. I wrote to remind him that the rigours of peer review of our papers and grant applications regularly serve to keep scientists grounded in reality and, occasionally, painful humility."

Writing his Reciprocal Space blog has taken Curry out into the world in ways that he never imagined, helping him to "redefine" his role as a professor and scientist. He blogged: "Of late, the focus of my writing has looped back into academia. A post I wrote last year to assess the importance of mathematics in the training of life scientists sparked an enormous response that is now helping me to organise a rethink of our curriculum."

Blogs are rarely literary masterpieces. Misspellings and punctuation errors abound. For example, Bongi, a South African general surgeon acclaimed in a headline as author of "The Best Doctor Blog on The Internet", writes about life on the boundaries between First World and Third World medicine. His neglect of literary convention would outrage pedants and grammarians, but he is a star storyteller. He has been blogging since 2006 without the apparent benefit of a shift key, but with passion, humour and humanity – for his own pleasure. As he put it: "I have a job that I do and do seriously. this is a hobby. if it became too much effort or too serious, i migh not enjoy it anymore."

How much, how often?

What about numbers? Most blog posts are probably between 300 and 500 words long; some exceed a 1,000 words or more. How often should you blog? Again, there are no set rules. Some bloggers post two or three times a week; others two or three times a month. The most widely read bloggers post regularly. The golden rule: have something to say – succinctly.

Journal blogs

The speed at which blogs can be published has encouraged journals such as the *BMJ* to publish their own blog posts by staff and freelance correspondents. This has not only brought new voices into the media arena. It has also extended the scope of published material. Journal blog posts extend from one extreme of the journalistic spectrum to the other – from hard news exclusives to the whimsical or historical. The option to be able to publish rapidly, and, critically, before a rival publication, appeals to editors. All editors like exclusives. Medical journal editors are no exception. [Also see Chapter Seven: *Writing for the media*].

Twitter

This chapter is about social media as a writing and communications tool, but social media have many other uses. For example, Twitter is good for:

News: Twitter can be used like real-time newspaper. Tweets often break news before the mainstream media. Journalists get most of their news from Twitter, but surprisingly, in October 2014, only one of my 35 postgraduate science students at the University of Cambridge regarded Twitter as a news channel.

Research: Twitter is a vast encyclopaedia of shared personal and professional experience.

Story ideas: More than 50% of journalists in a survey said that they used Twitter for new story ideas.[21]

New titles: Authors use Twitter to test out new title ideas.

Debate: Many conversations begin on Twitter.

Spreading the word: You can retweet useful tweets to your followers. Having a reputation as a sharer will enhance your online reputation.

Monitoring your public speaking performance: Follow the Twitter feed for your name and presentation at conferences.

Making conference notes: Tweeting key points can create a conference notebook.

Disseminating information and audio-visual material: Twitter links users to blog posts, professional and consumer forums, networks, lists, videos and photographs.

Journal club discussions: Twitter journal clubs include the UK-based Twitter Journal Club [twijc.com] and the Microbiology Twitter Journal Club [microtwjc.wordpress.com].

Talking points: Twitter highlights topical talking points in "What's trending?"

A no-strings office environment: For writers, artists, entrepreneurs and other lone workers, Twitter has all the benefits of an office environment without the downsides. You can leave Twitter at any time without upsetting anyone. No one will know if you're still in your dressing gown as the sun is going down. You can follow conversations as if you were a fly on the wall without opening your digital mouth. Just lurking is actually a good way to start Twitter – to feel your way around. Some people use it purely as a sounding board.

Following people

Twitter communities are made up of followers [people with mutual interests]. Registered users can read and post tweets and "follow" tweets by other registered users. Unregistered users can follow conversations by logging onto search.twitter.com. For example, type "Dr Kate Granger" into "search" to locate her page. Not all her tweets are about her campaign. For example, she tweeted a picture about the birth of a niece. This shows how social media can blur the boundaries between the personal and professional. Are such tweets irrelevant on such a site? Theory has it that such snapshots make tweeters feel more connected to one another. Really? Do people *really* want to hear about Granger's newborn niece? It would seem so. Granger's 36,000 plus followers [at the time of writing] could "unfollow" her if they chose. The longer they follow such people, the theory goes, the more connected they feel. The ultimate test is whether she adds value to their lives.

From snapshot to continuum

Unlike traditional media, Twitter and blogs can provide constant updates. As a print journalist I've written hundreds of case histories from the narrow perspective of one point in time – the interview date – and, at most, a two-hour conversation. Each interview has involved just two people, the interviewee and me, resulting in a snapshot – a still picture frozen in time. The Granger story as relayed by Twitter is more like a movie with special effects in the form of links to other blog posts, videos and pictures. It has unfolded over five years as a continuous conversation between tens of thousands of people. Followers ask questions, offer support, ignite debate, seek advice and tell stories of their own. A single tweet may be restricted to 140 characters, but the Granger Twitter story, including links, runs to tens of thousands of words.

Tweets about newborns may be acceptable, especially from someone such as Kate Granger. Tweets to flog things are not. People do not join Twitter for bargains or best buys, but to be part of a community with common interests. Before posting a tweet, ask yourself: how will this help my followers? For example, in 2014 I tweeted about an interview between the British Prime Minister David Cameron and the BBC *Newsnight* presenter Evan Davis, broadcast on his first night as the programme anchor.[22] I wanted to recommend this master class in interviewing to those who had missed it. Such posts may encourage followers to read my future tweets – and blogs.

What about tweeting to alert your followers to your latest blog post? Some bloggers tweet blog alerts once daily, others twice and some four. Knowing that viewers do not watch TV news around the clock, TV news channels have a similar repeat policy.

Health warnings

As discussed earlier, inexperienced media interviewees prefer telephone to TV or radio studio interviews, but they may say things in the comfort of home or office that they'd never say in the bright glare of a TV studio or in front of a microphone. The internet has a similar disinhibiting effect, with sometimes disastrous results. Before putting anything on line – I make no apology for repeating this advice – ask yourself: would I be happy saying this on live TV? The following would not have occurred if this advice had been heeded. A surgeon posted a photograph of his operating list to a medical-school friend on a public website. Naming the hospital, ten patients and other identifying material, the post was deemed to have breached patients' confidentiality.[23]

Similarly, a US hospital fired a 48-year-old doctor for posting information about an unnamed trauma patient on Facebook after a ruling that the patient was still identifiable.[24] Personal posts may also be damaging. An employment agency rejected a psychiatrist after she was shown topless and drinking from beer bongs on Myspace – even though the explicit pictures were eight years old and she had become fully qualified in the interim.[25] Restrict personal profiles on sites such as Facebook to private friends and family. Do not "friend" patients.

Defamation and libel

A theoretical plus of social media is that you can publish material without going through a middleman. In practice, middlemen have their place. At least five people, including an editor, will read this book before it is published because I know how easy it is to make simple mistakes. Equally importantly, I know the basics of libel law – thanks to McNae's *Essential Law for Journalists*.[26] There are similar guides in other countries. I was indebted to McNae and my journalism college law lecturer when I became an editor and hired a columnist who littered his copy with libels. He was an eloquent writer, but knew little libel law.

Defamation is defined as the communication of a false statement that harms the reputation of an individual, business, product, group, government or religion. Libel is defined as defamation by the *written* or *printed* or *broadcast* word. In 2013 a landmark UK case showed that online communications are not exempt. Lord McAlpine successfully alleged that he had been defamed by tweets implying that he was a paedophile. Many of these were retweets. Acting for McAlpine, solicitor Andrew Reid declared: "Twitter is not just a closed coffee shop among friends. It goes out to hundreds of thousands of people…

"It is not a place where you can gossip and say things with impunity and we are about to demonstrate that."[27] It is easy to be caught up in the sudden excitement of a Twitter storm such as the tweet – retweeted thousands of times – prematurely reporting the death of former UK Prime Minister Margaret Thatcher.

In 2014 a so-called Twitter "troll" was jailed for 18 weeks for sending abusive messages to the British Labour MP Stella Creasy after she had supported a successful campaign to put the writer Jane Austen on the £10 note. The prosecution told a City of London magistrates court that he had threatened to rape Creasy and called her a witch. In May 2015 he abandoned an appeal against his conviction. His lawyer said he had decided not to go ahead because his mother had been sick and he had childcare commitments as his partner had dumped him.

Tweeters and bloggers should also be mindful of employers who may disagree with what they say online, and potential employers who may check what they have already posted online. Deleting something from the internet – such as a blog post or a video – is not always easy. Most of the material people want deleted are things they posted maybe years earlier. Many websites' terms of use state that you lose rights in a post as soon as you post it. You will need a compelling reason to persuade a website to remove content. Regretting something that you put your name to previously, or disliking a comment about you, may not be enough.

Media monitoring
The Social Media Highway Code, published by the Royal College of General Practitioners, warned doctors that reporters may monitor their online activity to research stories. It added: "A number of journalists and media professionals expressed surprise at the online behaviour that they had witnessed from some doctors, citing occasional examples of doctors behaving in ways that they believed would be perceived as unprofessional by members of the public. One journalist referred to the online behaviour of some doctors as "naïve".

Examples were highlighted where conversations occurring on social media sites had led to stories in the national or trade press. "Journalists may, quite legitimately, approach doctors directly through social media sites to source stories or get a doctor's viewpoint. There may be a risk in public forums and microblogging sites, such as Twitter, of journalists attempting to engage doctors in discussions on sensitive or controversial issues, in the hope of provoking an unguarded response."[28]

The future
Dr Kate Granger's campaign is one of many examples showing how social media have swept aside the information barriers traditionally dividing doctors from patients. She did not realise how powerful her voice would become.

Would her campaign have taken off without the impetus of social media? Almost certainly not: traditional media campaigns do not create the communities and sense of inclusiveness that can give social media such an irrepressible head of steam. Nor do they allow continuing updates over long periods in the way that the internet uniquely does. The resounding success of her campaign brought Granger invitations to speak to a wide variety of audiences, including the media. Presenting to the media and other audiences is the theme of the next chapter.

SUMMARY

- Social media, digital word of mouth, enables healthcare professionals – and healthcare professionals and patients – to join forces in ways that would have been unthinkable in the pre-internet era.
- A blog presents writers with a dazzling, untethered type of freedom – without the protective constraints of peer review.
- The internet can have a disinhibiting effect. Never say anything online you would not be prepared to say on live TV.
- Writers can use Twitter in about 12 different ways. It offers a vast enclopaedia of shared personal and professional experience.
- In 2013 a landmark case showed that online communications are not exempt from libel law.

NOTES AND REFERENCES

1 http://drkategranger.wordpress.com/2013/09/04/hellomynameis/

2 https://www.england.nhs.uk/2014/01/30/kate-granger-2/

3 http://www.amazon.co.uk/The-Bright-Side-Kate-Granger-ebook/dp/B00906QZMC

4 https://storify.com/traumagasdoc/wrongfooted

5 *Health Service Journal* and *Nursing Times* (2014) http://www.nursingtimes.net/Journals/2014/05/28/x/w/g/NTSocialMedia_140530.pdf

6 Pho K, Gay S (2013) *Establishing, Managing, and Protecting Your Online Reputation: A Social Media Guide for Physicians and Medical Practices* Greenbranch Publishing

7 http://www.statisticbrain.com/twitter-statistics/

8 http://www.statista.com/statistics/272014/global-social-networks-ranked-by-number-of-users/

9 Twitter statistics www.statisticbrain.com/twitter-statistics (Accessed April 2015)

10 Royal College of General Practioners (2013) *Social Media Highway Code* p 5.

11 For a fuller list of leading blogs and websites go to:
http://lifeinthefastlane.com/resources/stuff-we-read (Website run by Australa-sian critical care physicians and nurses.)

12 Riley B, Gerada C (2013) *Social Media Highway Code* Royal College of General Practitioners p 11. The authors did find a number of specific circum-stances in which use of a pseudonym may be professionally appropriate.

13 McCartney M (2012) How much of a social media profile can doctors have? (citing Godwin Busuttil) *BMJ* 344:e440

14 Wikipedia en.wikipedia.org/wiki/Listicle

15 Chaplin S (2014) *Ten things GPs need to know about pharmacists* onlinelibrary.wiley.com/doi/10.1002/psb.1149/abstract

16 *The Guardian* was launched in 1821 as *The Manchester Guardian*, a weekly newspaper

17 digest.bps.org.uk/2010/07/bloggers-behind-blogs-dave-munger.html

18 http://sepsistrust.org/it-all-started-8-years-ago/

19 McCartney M (2012) How much of a social media profile can doctors have? *BMJ* 344:e440

20 Curry S (2013) Going Public: Professor Stephen Curry on blogging as an academic... www3.imperial.ac.uk/newsandeventspggrp/.../news_12-2-2013-15-48-6

21 www.poynter.org/.../most-journalists-now-get-story-ideas-from-social-m...

22 BBC Newsnight. October 29, 2014

23 Medical Defence Union (2013) http://www.themdu.com/guidance-and-advice/journals/mdu-journal-november-2013/disclosure-on-social-media

24 Wilner A (2011) Hospital Privileges Terminated Due to Facebook Post http://boards.medscape.com/forums/?128@@.2a090c48!comment=

25 Dolan PL (2008) Social networking etiquette: Making virtual acquaintances. *American Medical News* June 2. http://www.amednews.com/article/20080602/business/306029995/4/

26 McNae L *Essential Law for Journalists*. Oxford University Press. (In 2014 it was in its 22nd edition.)

27 Cheston P (2013) Humiliation for Sally Bercow as Speaker's wife faces £150,000 bill over Lord McAlpine libel tweet. London *Evening Standard.* May 24.

28 Riley M, Gerada C (2013) *Social Media Highway Code* Royal College of General Practitioners p 22

New media: a time to draw breath...

The previous chapter explores how social media and digital word of mouth are uniting healthcare professionals and patients in ways that would have been unthinkable only a few years ago. This is not just journalistic hype. It is truly remarkable, but let's not run away with ourselves. I want – on this solitary page – to draw breath. It is actually more of a triumph for technology than for human-to-human communication. Witness the way 'new media' interviewees and presenters duplicate the mistakes of their media predecessors. For example:

Filling the silence: As a healthcare professional you will know the potential advantage of not saying anything when a patient has answered a question. That patient may fill the silence by saying something really revealing. Media interviewees are the same and frequently say more than they initially intended, sometimes at great personal expense. Anticipate questions and decide how far to go in answering them. Establish firm boundaries. Say what you have to say and shut up. Let the interviewer fill the silence.

Speculating: Don't allow yourself to be drawn into speculating or hypothesising about future events. Speculation and hypothesis may mask your true position. Use a speculative question to bridge to where you want to go. [See Chapter Five: *Different types of interview*, page 66-6 for more on bridging.] While the interviewer picks the questions, you pick the answers, so long as you also address legitimate concerns.

Being overlong: Answer all questions in 30 seconds or fewer. Rehearse answers to see if you cut them to 15 seconds fewer. Treat email interviews in the same way. [By way of comparison, English-speaking TV presenters speak at about three words per second or 180 words per minute.]

Chapter 9

Presenting to the media and other audiences

Read this chapter to find out about:

PLANNING A TALK

PREPARING FOR QUESTION TIME

VISUAL AIDS

BODY LANGUAGE

FEAR OF PUBLIC SPEAKING

You may know colleagues who always seem to be on radio or TV. There will be two main reasons for this. First, they will be reliable. Broadcasting demands far more than fleeting, idiosyncratic brilliance. Second, they will be accomplished platform presenters. Good media interviewees and presenters know how to engage with and adjust to different audiences. They speak with passion and clarity. They know that scientific evidence will not speak for itself. If it did, there would be no need for meetings; everything could be done by email.

In contrast, many naturally animated people undergo a stifling metamorphosis on the podium. Perhaps medical science has yet to exorcise the ghost of passivity that took possession of it in the early 20th century when the passive voice was perceived to be objective, impersonal and more appropriate for science writing and presentation.

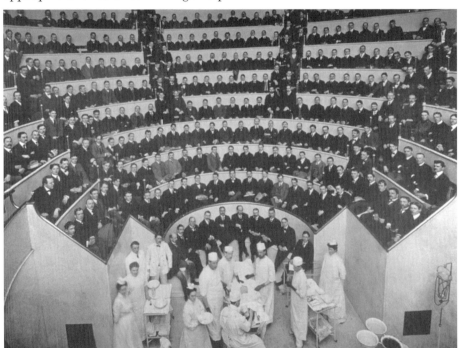

Photo credit: *Stanley B. Burns MD and the Burns Archive*
The passive voice may have been perceived as objective, impersonal and more appropriate for science presentation in the early 19th century, but pioneer surgeons such as William Rodman recognised the power of the active and the personal and used photography as a silent means of promoting themselves and their profession. Images like this showing him demonstrating his latest technique for treating cancer to an audience of more than 200 people in Philadelphia in 1902 said far more than words could ever say about his reputation. Hospitals displayed such pictures on public view as prominently as possible.

Fashion, of course, is fickle. The active voice urged by George Orwell [page 104] is back in vogue. For example, the *BMJ* style guide politely requests: "Please write in a clear, direct and active style." However, Peter Fiske, author of *Put Your Science to Work*, observed, "Although scientists may increasingly write their papers in the active voice, the way they promote their work often remains passive. Scientists expect their publications to communicate for them.

A large body of scholarly work certainly confers a degree of authority and knowledge. But even the best-written papers never completely capture the passion and insight that led to their creation. Scientists must communicate about their work to other scientists, sponsors of their research and the general public."[1]

Bloggers are doing just this – and shaking up medical and science writing. Speakers should also do more to engage with audiences. I am trying to encourage this process. For example, Nancy Mendoza[2] and I have been teaching communication skills to postgraduate science students at the University of Cambridge for eight years. We stress the importance of students going out into the world and demonstrating commitment and enthusiasm for their work and its life-enhancing potential. Most people don't understand the complexities of disciplines such as nanotechnology, but they warm to passion and to engaging people. Conversely, they may not trust dispassionate people. Highlighting the importance of engagement some 2,500 years ago, Aristotle, the father of rhetoric, suggested that there were three parameters of persuasion:

Logos: An appeal to logic; persuading by reason.
Ethos: An appeal to ethics; persuading the audience of the speaker's authority and credibility.
Pathos: An appeal to emotion.

Planning your talk
Where do I begin? As mentioned in Chapter Four [*Preparing for a media interview*], "Begin with the end in mind" is one of the *7 Habits of Highly Effective People*[3] cited by US management guru Stephen R Covey in his bestseller of that name.

What do I want the audience to do afterwards? Good talks are catalysts of change. For example, a diabetes self-help group established invaluable local media contacts after I had spoken to them about working with reporters.

Who will the audience be? Pitching a talk either "too high" or "too low" is rude. For example, my wife recently complained about a prominent professor who "spoke down" to senior nurses, using slides written for an introductory medical student lecture. Establish:

- How many people will be in the audience
- Their common interests and expectations
- How much they know about your subject
- What they want and need to know
- If anyone might object to your talk or see you as a threat.

What's my message(s)? Knowing the audience and what you want them to do helps to develop change-generating messages. Chapter Four [*Preparing for a media interview*] and Chapter Five [*Different sorts of interview*] have more on defining objectives, developing messages and anticipating and handling questions.

How do I prepare for question time? Devote at least 40 per cent of preparation time to anticipating questions and developing answers – one unanticipated question can torpedo all the hard work of a good presentation. Identifying tough questions may also produce a better talk. Prepare honest responses to unanswerable questions. For example: "We don't have the answer, but we're working on it." Don't sidestep controversy hoping that it will go away. Addressing it head on in the presentation itself may pre-empt hostile questions.

There is a section on answering *questions* later in this chapter.

Structure
This should reflect:

- What you want to say
- How much time you have
- How much the audience can take in.

Reconciling these aims and limitations isn't easy. The more you say the less the audience will take in. They will quickly forget most of it unless it is earth shattering or affects them personally. [How much can you remember from the last ten talks you attended?] Repeated messages are more likely to stick. Restrict yourself to no more than three messages or main points, repeating them, if possible, in different ways, two or three times.

Three-part structures are popular – yes, the power of three again. For example, problem, cause, solution; past, present, future; safety, efficacy, cost effectiveness; or the best known:

- Tell them what you're going to tell them
- Tell them
- Tell them that you have told them.

This structure can be used to describe a hypothesis, methods to test it and results. Think of it as being like an onion. The outer layer represents what you are going to say – your message. Stripping away that layer adds depth to

"The first principle of understanding language is elementary but widely misunderstood."

your talk and returns to the same points and message(s). It is simple, and it's easy to follow. Simple does not mean low quality. Simplifying means amplifying. Described by Leonardo da Vinci as the ultimate sophistication, simplicity means paring things down to bare essentials, eliminating redundant detail and recognising that the written word is much better than the spoken word for communicating complex data. An audience cannot go back if they lose their way. This is why repetition is important. There is much to commend the veteran editor who told a junior journalist: "KISS! Remember to KISS." (Keep it simple, stupid!) A more polite version is: "Keep it simple and straightforward". As the character in the cartoon on the previous page observes, this involves elementary principles, but how often do we see speakers straying from the elementary?

Planning with a storyboard

Preferring to think onto paper rather than onto a computer screen, many writers, filmmakers, computer geeks and speakers create storyboards with Post-it labels representing individual slides or points. A storyboard is a graphic point-by-point representation of a talk or book or movie. Most people find it is easier to move Post-it notes around a table or wall than to go from normal view to slide sorter on a computer. Another option is a graph plotting each part of your talk on a three-part grid.

First impressions

You can lose an audience within 20 seconds by not making a good first impression. Good starters include:

A provocative question: For example, have you ever considered euthanasia?

A powerful statistic: For example, people who live to 90 will spend 32 years or 36 per cent of their lives asleep.

A challenging quotation: For example, in an introduction to a prescribing habits debate I quoted Sir William Osler, a Canadian physician and one of the founders of the US John Hopkins Hospital in Baltimore: "We all have our therapeutic ruts, and we all know consultants from whom patients find it very difficult to escape without their favourite prescription, no matter what the malady may be."

"You": One of the most powerful words in the English language, "you" appeals to our favourite subject and closes the gap between speaker and audience. For example, Dr Atul Gawande, the 2014 Reith Lecturer and bestselling author, began a commencement address at Yale Medical School on May 24, 2004 with seven references to "you" or"your" in the opening paragraph.

A memorable story: For example, Gawande started his first BBC Reith Lecture by recalling the moment he discovered his 11-day old son had a heart problem. Every parent would have been able to identify with this compelling introduction.

Last impressions

A good first impression grabs attention. A good last impression makes people change how they do or see things. Aim to finish early to avoid rushing the conclusion, the most critical part of your talk. This will allow time not only to sum up your results, but also to explain what makes them so important. It may further allow more time for questions and create additional opportunities to take the audience with you. Being able to interact directly with peers during question time is part of what makes a meeting special. It brings people together in a way that a written paper cannot. Many people squander this opportunity, leaving themselves short of time, giving the impression that they have lost control.

Accomplished presenters commit introductory and concluding remarks to memory so that they can address audiences directly at these make or break points. This does not mean quoting a script word for word – as I wrote earlier, this may make you sound stilted. Just know what you want to say and how you want to say it. Written four-or five-word headings may help. Short sentences are best – this is no time for long monologues. Alliteration can add impetus and stick in the memory. For example, the SunSmart health campaign with its slogan: Slip! Slop! Slap! [Slip on a shirt, slop on the sunscreen, slap on a hat] was one of the most successful in Australian history.

Voice

It can be alarming to hear a recording of yourself for the first time. Vibrations in the skull make us think our voices are lower and fuller in pitch than they actually are. As they travel through the bone they spread out and lower in pitch, giving a false sense of bass. A voice recorder is not the only way to find out how we sound to others. You may have been accused of sounding aggressive, rude or abrupt when you felt nothing of the kind. Presentation-skills-training participants are often shocked to find out that they sound bored and monotonous or that they have a pronounced accent. Fortunately, the first things are usually easy to correct and a distinctive accent is rarely a problem if the speaker is clearly understood.

Breathing: Please excuse this basic physiology lesson and bear with me. Good breathing is the key to a good voice, according to Cicely Berry, former voice director of the Royal Shakespeare Company.[4] Breath initiates sound by striking the vocal cords, making them vibrate: the firmer the force of breath, the truer the sound. Conversely, the shallower the breath, the more muffled the sound.

Breathing slowly and deeply should make you feel better and more confident, producing a richer, more expansive sound. Standing upright, with head held high, shoulders pulled in and a straight back will open up your chest and encourage deep breathing from the diaphragm. You may know all this, but how many times have you heard colleagues who seem to have forgotten it?

Pace: Breath is not only the voice's fuel; it can also be used as a brake and accelerator. Breathing slowly and deeply stops you speaking too quickly. Alas, there must be as many presenters breaking the oral speed limit as there are drivers doing so on the road. Optimal speaking speed varies from person to person. Gawande's first Reith Lecture began at between two and three words a second – the first 66 words in just under 30 seconds. English-speaking TV presenters speak at about three words per second or 180 words a minute; good slide presenters at about 125 words per minute. I like Gawande's slow, conversational style. He seems to have all the time in the world, but he is too slow for my wife, Liz. This was the first complaint I'd heard about a public speaker being too slow! Trial and error will show what works best for you, but no one, not even Gawande, will please everyone.

Avoid oral cruise control – going the same speed all the time. Listen to how professional broadcasters speed up towards the climax of a story and slow down for moments of reflection or complex information, reserving the slowest delivery for the most difficult content. Note how the stress on particular words and phrases emphasises key points and enhances aural variety.

Pitch: Slow, controlled breathing affects pitch, the degree of highness or lowness in our voices. We tend to a higher pitch when we are nervous or excited; a lower one when we are relaxed and in control. Low-pitched voices are synonymous, rightly or wrongly, with leadership and gravitas. Breathing from your diaphragm and speaking slowly and deliberatively will give you a lower pitch and a deeper voice. You can practise this gradually: take care not to strain your vocal cords. Try to vary your pitch as well as speaking speed. Pitch is like music, full of high and low notes. It's variety that makes it attractive. Changing pitch can convey different shades of meaning, such as surprise or emphasis.

Passion: You don't have to scream or be histrionic to register passion. Just talk as if you really mean it. Don't try to imitate others. Trying to be someone else won't work. Develop your own style. You don't have to be slick, brilliant and witty. It won't matter if you get tongue tied and make mistakes if you say something of value in the right way. Listen to the way professional broadcasters handle their mistakes, sometimes with humour, before moving seamlessly on.

Pause: Great orators know the power of well-timed pause. Not to be confused with hesitation, a controlled pause is a device for connecting with your audience to create a sense of emphasis or anticipation – or whatever. The writer and orator Mark Twain declared: "The right word may be effective, but no word is ever as effective as the rightly timed pause." This is as true of a scientific talk as of Shakespeare.

A two or three second pause can help to:
- Give you time to catch your breath and stop you going too fast. Breathing deeply as they pause gives many speakers a sense of taking control.
- Inject aural variety into your speech and stop you flat-lining and sounding monotonous.

- Highlight key points: it gives the audience time to absorb – it's another way of saying *this is really important.*

Body language

You may know what you are saying, but what is your body saying? Verbal and gestural vocabularies need to be aligned to connect with your audience. Think of your body as being like a loudspeaker that will amplify what you say if your verbal and gestural vocabularies are working in tandem and distort it if they are not.

Eye contact: This is the most effective form of human communication, irrespective of whether you're speaking to one person or a group. Eye contact

- Initiates communication
- Inspires trust
- Keeps listeners focused on you, helping you to stay in control
- Puts people at ease, making them feel the centre of attention
- Helps to control anxiety if you focus your eyes on one person.

You may be tempted in a talk to focus on people nodding approval, but try to take in the entire room – especially the less enthusiastic. Eye contact may be your best chance to win them over. Don't focus too much on any one individual – this may embarrass them and confuse the rest of the audience. Imagine yourself as a submarine commander making a gentle 180-degree sweep with your periscope. Establishing eye contact may be impossible in a large hall or under the harsh glare of bright lights, but the stage manager may be able to adjust the lights so you and your audience can see one another. This may not be possible in the event of filming.

Gestures: I recall a speaker whose hands went rhythmically up and down as if he were milking a cow. There was no relation between these dairyman-like antics and what he was saying, making it hard to follow. He would have been shocked to see himself on camera – as would many other presenters who, for example, nod furiously in response to a hostile question when they should be shaking their heads in a display of gentle disagreement.

Gestures should "fit" the room as well as "fitting" and amplifying your words. I speak a lot with my hands, perhaps because I started my career playing

Shakespeare and learnt about the value of expansive gestures – with arms spread wide, for example. In a big hall such gestures should begin from the shoulder, not the wrist or the elbow as they do in everyday conversation.

Many presenters don't know what to do with their hands. If this is you, bend your elbows and bring your hands together into neutral positions at a hand clapping or crotch level. Alternatively, put your hands by your sides – another neutral position. Practise going from one neutral position to another and then extending your hands in front of your body to emphasise a point. Letting your hands fall to your sides between gestures creates a confident impression.

It's not only hands that can go absent without leave. Without knowing it, I kept swinging my right leg upwards and outwards every ten to 15 seconds during a presentation at the huge O2 London arena. I might have got away with it if the lectern hadn't been transparent. Rehearsals can resolve such blips. Try filming a rehearsal, ideally before honest colleagues or friends or family members. This may be stressful but it's better than having your limbs go AWOL at a big meeting. It's critical in a rehearsal to talk the talk – not just to think it. What reads well and looks good to the eye may not sound well to the ear. Again, practice makes us all better.

Stance: People see you before they hear you. Your gait and stance can shout "I am confident" or "I am really uncomfortable". Practise [that word yet again] maintaining a balanced stance, with weight even but slightly forward, and feet pointing straight ahead, not quite shoulder-width apart. Focus on standing still and not swaying around – a major distraction. Of course you can move

Photo credit: ©*Monkey Business/Shutterstock.com*
Presenters should not be afraid to step out from behind the lectern. The closer you can get to an audience, the better.

around, especially in a small room. The closer you are to your audience
the easier it is to engage with them. The sooner you do so the better. For
example, I was recently part of a group of 15 people arriving for a meeting.
The speaker could have sat apart, making last-minute adjustments to
her talk. But she was at the door, greeting her prospective audience with
a smile, a handshake and eye contact. She created the impression of an
in-control person who really wanted to help us. She continued to engage
us directly, leaving the lectern for a centre-stage position close to us from
where she could move quickly left or right or up and down to address
anyone of us directly.

Anxiety

I tell nervous speakers: "Speaking as the author of *Beat Panic and Anxiety*,[5]
I'm glad you feel anxious. It's the fearless people who worry me." A major
cause of anxiety is the fear that something will go wrong, but, though it
sounds glib to say it, thorough preparation can be the antidote to that fear.

There is a narrow divide between healthy concern and panic-inducing
anxiety. Trial and error will determine what's best to help you to retain
control. I never give a talk without a glass of water to hand because I am
prone to a dry mouth. I take a deep breath before starting a talk and try to
talk slowly, but not too slowly. I write "slow" at the top of my notes. I take
further deep breaths and pause after making critical points. It may be
illusionary, but this gives me a sense of control. Breathing exercises and
relaxation techniques work for other people. Rehearsal works for everyone
and helps to build competence, which in turn builds confidence, which in
turn builds credibility.

Visual aids

Visual aids can increase understanding and clarity, but too much visual
information creates confusion and clutter. Visual aids include:

Handouts: A talk should present the big picture. A handout can add the small
print. Handouts work best with small groups. Announce if a handout is
available, to avoid unnecessary note taking. Distributing it beforehand
may distract attention from your talk if audience members keep consulting
them instead of listening to what you have to say.

Flip charts: These are a very effective way to engage an audience. Check that the back row can read them. They also work best in small groups but can be filmed for display on big screens.

Props: A good prop will engage an audience. For a master class in prop use and making health and economic data sing, see Hans Rosling, professor of international health at the Karolinska Institute, Stockholm. His props include IKEA storage boxes, a washing machine, a sword, and bar graphs made from stones. The end of this chapter has links to his presentations.

The ABC of slides and word play

A Anticipate: Consider the audience's needs before your own.

B Background: Keep slide backgrounds simple. I use a plain background and logo, but some critics say that logos clutter slides.

C Contrast: High-contrast slides are easier to read. For example, black text against a white background and white text against a blue background work well; green on red and white on grey do not. Colour-blind people cannot

ABSTRACT

Genetic factors, in particular Human Leucocyte Antigens (HLA), are important determinants of susceptibility to sarcoidosis. To clarify the role of HLA in this disease, we determined HLA-DRB1 phenotype data for case-control samples from three distinct European populations (UKCaucasian, Polish Slavonic, and Czechs), and compared these with published data from three additional populations (Italians, Japanese, and Scandinavians). Reductions in the frequency of HLA-DR1 and -DR4 alleles were remarkably consistent in all six populations suggesting a"protective"effect. Comparison of protein sequences for all HLA-DRB1 alleles identified the position 11 residue properties as differing between protective (-DR1, -DR4) and non-protective

alleles: protective alleles had hydrophobic sidechains (HR), which were not found in non-protective alleles. HLA-DRB1 Position 11 residues are the sole variable residue within the P6 pocket of the HLA-DR peptide binding groove, therefore determining this pockets peptide binding preferences. We combined our three study samples in a stratified analysis and found that sarcoidosis cases had a highly significant reduction in the HLA-DRB1 HR alleles ($c2=24.6, d.f.=2, P=0.0000007$), yielding a Mantel-Haenszel weighted OR of 0.56 (0.44-0.70). Whether the protective effect of HLA-DRB1 HR alleles is due to enhanced binding of a foreign antigen or diminished binding of an autoantigen is unclear, as the disease causing antigenic stimulus remains undetermined.

Slide credit: *Ron du Bois from his talk, The short [ten minute] presentation.*
There is a big difference between a talk and a written academic paper. A talk should distil the main points of a paper. It should not be presented in the style of a journal abstract. The 200-word abstract in the above slide would have been better broken down into two or even three slides. PowerPoint is designed as a visual aid to complement the spoken word. It is better at conveying the big picture than small detail. Bar charts, pie charts and ribbon charts should makes slides easier to understand. Journal-paper readers can go at their own pace, fast or slow, unlike an audience that has to keep up with the speaker.

distinguish between reds and greens of the same magnitude of brightness.

D Data: Don't write a presentation as if it were a journal article. An audience can take in only so much. Include as little data as possible but as much as is necessary to reach your goal.

E Examples: Specific examples such as case histories help to bring a presentation to life.

F Font: Sans-serif fonts such as Arial, Helvetica, Tahoma and Verdana are easy to read.

G Graph: Don't crowd graphs. Turn a single cluttered graph into two or even three clear ones.

H Hidden agenda: Will anyone in the audience have one? Prepare robust answers to possible tough questions.

I Interaction: The right kind of interaction between speaker and audience can lift a talk beyond the sum of its parts.

J Jargon: This is useful – if the audience understands it. This underlines the importance of knowing your audience. Inappropriate use of jargon is common.

K Knowledge: Don't assume audiences know more – or less – than they do.

L Large: Font size must be large enough to be easily read: 40 point is the preferred size for titles and 32 point for most text. Never use anything smaller than 18 point.

M Message: Remember the power of three. Restrict yourself to a maximum of three messages.

N Novelty: What's new or *different* about your talk? Let the audience know. Signpost key points and messages.

O Outcome: The most important thing is not the talk itself, but the outcome.

P PowerPoint: Use as few slides as possible for maximum impact.

Q Questions: See below.

R References: Keep them small and to a minimum to limit clutter.

S Slides: Make them simple and clear, using no more than 13-14 for a ten-minute presentation, while looking at the audience, not at the slides. Audiences sight-read slides more quickly than you can say them, so don't read them verbatim. Build on them.

T Title: Most slides should have a clear title.

U Upbeat: Upbeat presenters engage audiences.

V Video: Short clips can highlight medical and surgical procedures and bring patient case histories to life in a way that words and pictures cannot.

W White space: Originally a newspaper term, white space is the portion of

SUMMARY OF RESULTS ACHIEVED

h Susceptibility to CFA may be denoted by co-carriage of specific polymorphisms in interleukin-6 and tumour necrosis factor receptor II when compared with controls.

h More severe disease may be associated a specific polymorphism in interleukin 6.

h Susceptibility may be associated with increase in specific polymorphic combinations in glutathione s-transferase P.

h Several of the different GST polymorphisms are associated with each other as well as with gender and smoking status

h All polymorphisms within the same gene are in linkage with each other.

h Polymorphisms in antioxidant enzymes apart from glutathione s-transferase are not involved in CFA

n **susceptibility to CFA associated with**
   4 **co-carriage of TNFR II and IL-6 polymorphisms**
   4 **glutathione s-transferase polymorphisms**

n **more severe disease with IL-6 + 258 polymorphism**

n **CFA not associated with**
   4 **antioxidant enzyme polymorphisms**

Photo credit: *Ron du Bois from his talk, The short [ten minute] presentation.*
Both these slides summarise the talk, but note how the second has more impact by virtue of being shorter. The author has simplified the content, paring it down to the bare essentials. Simple does not mean low quality. Simplifying means amplifying, a process Leonardo da Vinci described as the ultimate sophistication. According to one view, PowerPoint slides should follow the "the rule of six": [no more than six lines per slide and no more than six to eight words per line]. This is over-rigid - but remember that it is hard to read text and listen to a speaker at the same time.

a page or slide left unmarked or white. The more white space, the more attention is drawn to the content. Thus five words will have more impact than 15.

X: X marks the spot where you want to be at the end of your talk – and where you want the audience to go.

Y You: Evaluate your performance with audience feedback forms. Seek further comments from trusted friends or colleagues.

Z Zen: Presentation Zen[6] by Garr Reynolds advocates restraint, simplicity, clarity and brevity.

Answering questions

Presentations end with question time – as does this chapter. As I said earlier, one unanticipated question can sabotage an otherwise successful presentation. This is why I recommend devoting at least 40 per cent of preparation time to question time. In answering questions:

Thank each delegate for their question: Don't commend "good" questions. People asking lesser questions may be put out if you don't commend them.

Repeat the question: The classic reason given for repeating a question is to allow you time to think through your answer. But if you are properly prepared, you will have anticipated the question and worked out your answer. There is no such thing as a difficult question if you have a prepared answer, but the simplest of questions may be unsettling if you haven't. However, repeating the question gives the audience a second chance to hear it if they missed it, a common occurrence, and presents an opportunity for clarification if *you* misheard it.

Keep your cool: Never insult a rude or hostile questioner. Defuse the situation by saying something such as: "We can't agree now, but I'd welcome the opportunity to talk later. In the meantime, I suggest we take further questions."

Prepare honest responses to unanswerable questions. Admit you don't know the answer.

Messages: Question time is an opportunity to repeat your key messages, perhaps by using the ABC bridging technique discussed in Chapter Five:

Different forms of interview. Bridging is well recognised as a technique to deploy in media interviews, but it can also be used in many other settings – from question time to job interviews.

TED Talks

TED [Technology, Entertainment and Design] features dozens of examples of state-of-the-art scientific presentations. [ted.com]. These include talks by the props master Professor Hans Roslin. The annual TED Conference features many of the world's greatest thinkers and doers in 18-minute talks. This time limit encourages concise, tightly focused presentations.

SUMMARY

- Although many healthcare professionals and scientists increasingly write papers in the active voice, the way they promote their works remains passive. They need to do more to engage audiences.
- People are good at remembering and conceptualising things in threes. This is what makes three-part presentation structures effective. For example: past, present, future; problem, cause, solution; safety, efficacy, cost effectiveness.
- One unforeseen question can undo all the hard work of an otherwise excellent presentation. Dedicating 40 per cent of preparation time to anticipating questions and developing answers minimises this risk. Identifying tough questions may also improve your talk and pre-empt controversial questions.
- Simple does not mean low quality. Simplifying (reportedly described by Leonardo da Vinci as "the ultimate sophistication") means amplifying.
- You can lose an audience within 20 seconds by not making a good first impression.
- A good last impression will make people change how they do or see things.

NOTES AND REFERENCES

1   Fiske P (2010) Speak up. *Nature* www.nature. com/naturejobs/science/articles/10.1038/nj7286-312a

2   Nancy Mendoza is a communications consultant.

3   Covey S (1989) *The 7 Habits of Highly Effective People* Simon & Schuster

4   Berry C (2003) *Your Voice & How to Use It* Virgin Books

5   Illman J (2006) *Beat Panic & Anxiety* Cassell Illustrated

6   Reynolds G (2008) *Presentation Zen: Simple Ideas on Presentation Design and Delivery* New Riders

Chapter 10

Media case histories. A suitable case for treatment

Read this chapter to find out about:

THE VALUE OF CASE HISTORIES

THEIR MISUSE

ABUSE OF PATIENT INTERVIEWEES

ADVICE FOR PATIENT INTERVIEWEES

AN ALTERNATIVE CASE-HISTORY MODEL

Storytelling is an integral part of our culture. From a very young age we listen to and tell stories. Virtually every culture, religion and tradition uses storytelling in teaching. Medical stories are encapsulated in case histories in both medical education and medical journalism. They help us to define ourselves and to compare ourselves with others, giving a sense of perspective about our place in the scheme of things.

Dr William J Donnelly, of the Edward Hines Jr VA Hospital, Illinois, observed: "Case histories matter. These narratives are the way in which physicians at every level of training communicate to each other their understanding of particular patients and their medical problems, what has been done about the problems, and what is being done about them."[1]

Consumer-media case histories can help patients to learn from one another about what to expect physically and mentally. They can also enable healthcare professionals to take a leap of imagination into the patient's shoes, into what it is really like to feel vulnerable, at risk and dependent. A good consumer case history blends the objective knowledge of medical science with the patient's subjective experience, but the compiling of media case histories is driven by conflicting agendas that can conspire against patient interviewees and media audiences. Patients need to be made more aware of the potential hazards of working with the media.

Vulnerable patients
The media use medical case histories to generate audiences and advertising. Hospitals, charities and patient groups use them to raise profiles, recruit new patients, encourage donations and attract research funds. Some patient groups are funded by pharmaceutical and healthcare companies who also have vested interests.

And what about patients? What's in it for them? Some interviewees want to help other patients or a hospital or charity. Others seek attention. Some like to have a legitimate reason to talk to a stranger, someone outside of friends and family, even if this will expose them to an audience of millions. Some are just curious. But imagine talking to a total stranger about your depression or heart disease or cancer or erectile dysfunction, when what you say will be edited, published and possibly elicit a negative response from a relative, neighbour, or from an employer if there is a question about your fitness to work.

Most subjects do little if anything to prepare for such interviews. This means, among other things, that they may fail to establish no-go areas. This may not matter in the case of a verruca, but what about a psychological or sexual problem? For example, a young doctor, who went on to receive one of the UK's highest honours, spoke to me at great length about his previous suicidal feelings. Ambushed by my questions he commented, as so many people do: "I don't know why I am telling you all of this." This was not the reason for the interview and I did not report it. I felt like a priest at a confession.

This kind of reaction – the exact opposite of what might be predicted – is extremely common. Interviewees are more likely to be trusting and impulsive than guarded and cautious. Media interviews can even produce, like psychoanalysis, regressive reactions.[2]

This happens even though journalist and patient have different agendas. Patients may be unaware of these conflicting aspirations. Journalists, for the very best of reasons, try to establish a rapport with patient interviewees. They want interviewees to trust them. In their turn patients want to trust people with whom they may be sharing their innermost fears and concerns. Reputable journalists try to produce case histories that reconcile this trust with demand from editors for case histories that are rich in "news values" [described in Chapter Two: *The news business* and other criteria described below].

There is now another means of publication for patients, free from the straitjacket of the news-values culture. Patient groups can publicise case histories on their own websites and maintain full editorial control. These "stories" tend to put more emphasis on practical problems for specific groups than broader, sometimes emotionally charged stories written for wider audiences. The traditional news-values model, let me stress, is not being eclipsed – at least, not yet. It is still predominant because the consumer media, unlike patient-group websites, have audiences that reach out to millions via a myriad of platforms – from Twitter and Facebook to radio and TV. [There is more about patient group websites later in this chapter.]

Ethics and journalists

Most journalists recognise the vulnerability of patients. These questions, for example, were discussed in a Guild of Health Writers case study workshop in the UK:[3]

- Where do you discover people who will talk openly and intelligently about their medical history and personal health problems?
- How candid should you ask them to be?
- When is it appropriate to use pseudonyms?
- What should you do if you are asked to read back your copy?
- Do we have an ethical responsibility to protect those who may be too naïve to realise the implications of their revelations? Are there some things that just should not go into print?
- And what do you when the editor rejects the story that is so important to them?
- Or appears, but not quite as you wrote it?

Note: Most media case histories *do not* cause concern or offence. Most probably have desirable outcomes, but some of the following examples highlight the vulnerability of patients. This is an under-researched area. The first example is one of good practice.

The power of one

Clare Oliver, 26, died from melanoma in Melbourne in 2007.[4] In the last month of her life she underlined the danger of sunbeds – the cause of her cancer – in a campaign prompting about 100 press articles and nearly 400 broadcasts. Supported by the Victoria health minister, the state premier and federal health minister, Oliver seemed to achieve in days what others had been trying for many years. The *BMJ* described her story as a powerful example of how an individual could enlist the media to shape public health policy. It was also important, the *BMJ* noted, that the evidence for such policy had already been established, enabling swift government action.[5] [The Victoria government had been collecting sunbed data for more than a decade.]

Stephen Sutton, aged 19, enlisted media help to raise money. He died in May 2014 after raising more than £3.2 million for the UK Teenage Cancer Trust after news of his plight spread on social media. Diagnosed with bowel cancer at the age of 15, he drew up a "bucket list" of 46 "weird and wonderful" things to do before he died. He completed a sky dive and played drums to an audience of 90,000 people before the UEFA Champions League soccer final in London.

What makes such stories so powerful? Mother Teresa of Calcutta had the answer. Able to communicate with anyone from politicians, dignitaries and world leaders to the poorest beggars, she is reported to have said: "If I look at the mass, I will never act. If I look at the one, I will."

In 1987, "Baby Jessica" received more than $700,000 in public donations after falling into a well in Texas. More than £275,000 was raised for Ali Abbas, a child wounded in the Iraq war. These examples of the Mother Teresa effect are cited in research into what persuades people to donate to charity.[6] The results may dismay researchers and clinicians who rely on the power of numbers – the statistical, the methodological, the analytical and the objective. The better statistically informed the potential donors were, the less money they gave. People who read a short emotional appeal about an African child at risk from hunger gave more than twice as much as those who just saw raw statistics about the threat to millions of Africans. The facelessness of statistics, a major strength in science, can be an abject weakness in public relations.

Statistics, it seems, encourage analytical thinking, blunt emotions and turn people off. This is why charities invite donors to sponsor a specific child and why the media focus on individual case histories. To do otherwise would be to try to buck a trend as old as human life itself. Individual-based stories, a source of derision among many scientists, are not an invention of the modern media or of modern charities. Reliance on anecdotes, for all their shortcomings – about which, more shortly – are a big part of what makes us human.

The strength of the Clare Oliver story was that it combined traditional storytelling with a strong evidence base. The same was said to be true of the South African TV soap opera *Soul City* – case histories don't have to be real to have an impact. Tackling major health issues such as HIV/AIDS, the series is reported to have saved lives, and to have attracted more than 34 million viewers, nearly 70 per cent of the population, one in ten of whom had HIV/AIDS, according to a *BMJ* report.[7] Good drama, as Tennessee Williams observed is "truth in the pleasant disguise of illusion".[8] *Soul City* was just that – a creative alliance between scientists and artists.

Ethics and charities

Good drama packs an emotional punch, as do dramatic real-life stories that highlight ethical dilemmas. For example, the UK charity Macmillan Cancer Support invited Tony Bonser to talk on radio about how his 35-year-old son had died from cancer.[9] The interview coincided with the launch of a report into dying at home. Neil disliked hospitals and wanted to die at home. Macmillan helped him to do so. His father explained how he watched the fear, pain and stress leave Neil's face when they got home. He died peacefully. An official charity spokesperson may have lacked Bonser's conviction and credibility. Third-party endorsements like this carry weight – and raise cash.

Such interviews have clear benefits, but what's more important in fund raising – the worthiness of the cause or the emotional power of the communications strategy? A credible third-party spokesperson such as Tony Bonser could speak about one charity, unaware that another was doing an even better job. This is a potential weak link in the modern communication chain, but no one, I believe, has found a better alternative. In saying this I recognise that Macmillan's reputation as a leading charity is richly deserved.

The state-funded Birmingham Children's Hospital in the UK raised more than £2 million in 2009/2010 to develop new treatments and additional services. Placing stories about child patients in the media is part of the hospital's fund-raising policy. Big headlines may bring big returns, but not without potential risks to young patients and their families.

Speaking in 2011,[10] Alan Taman, the hospital's communications editor, recalled a child who had been injured by a police car. The story made headlines. TV soap-opera stars visited the child in hospital. Reporters "laid siege" to the family home. The hospital obtained invaluable press coverage

– not of its own making – but at what cost to the family? Can parents in shock make informed judgements about how to handle the media? What are the risks to the young patient? Taman's experience has convinced him that parents with no experience of how the media work are vulnerable.

In another case a mother wanted a newspaper to photograph her injured child in hospital. The hospital dissuaded her. Taman recalled: "My judgement was that this would have been wrong because the child had a facial injury. There could have been adverse repercussions." Taman compiled hospital guidelines for media handling after this case.

Dr Oliver Gillie, formerly *The Sunday Times* medical correspondent in the UK, described an interview with a child in an iron lung, another story with fund-raising potential.[11] Gillie was accompanied by the distinguished war photographer Sally Soames shortly after she had seen a colleague die in a guided-missile attack. He recalled: "She was extremely tough, but after being in that hospital, she said she never wanted to do another medical story. The hospital and the parents had given us permission to proceed, but the child was clearly distressed. I'm not sure how he was briefed for the interview. He obviously felt extremely uncomfortable. We could not establish eye contact with him."

In the USA patients are used as pawns in hospital marketing operations, according to Trudy Lieberman of the *Columbia Journalism Review*. She told a conference that one hospital had paid $1.5 million to a local TV station to broadcast a weekly package of stories about sick children.[12] This was a variation of a practice that had become widespread in the US and that crossed the traditional barrier separating paid-for advertising from independent news. Under contracts between hospitals and TV stations, reporters were forbidden to consult with experts from other hospitals or research institutions "as good journalists were supposed to do". The American Hospital Association condemned the practice as "an unwelcome result of fierce marketplace competition in healthcare".[13]

The curse of the media anecdote

Stories like these lend additional credence to the complaint by Professor Raymond Tallis, a former professor of geriatric medicine at the University of Manchester, now a writer, about "the curse of the media anecdote". He criticised "the habit of giving appealing individuals with their moving stories at least as much credence and coverage as unappealing data, of preferring faces to graphs, and vox pops to statistics".[14] The anecdote may be an imperfect tool, but what are the alternatives in the consumer arena? Communication via p-values and confidence intervals resonate with only a small minority. The real problem is not the anecdote, but its misuse. Is there a risk, as Tallis suggests, that a powerful emotional case will outweigh objective scientific evidence and result in a wrong turn? Yes – of course. The challenge is in achieving balance, as in the Clare Oliver story and in *Soul City*.

Sensationalism

This heart-sink editor's request is fictional, but it will strike a chord with reporters. "Can you find a 35-ish, attractive, single-parent paraplegic with diabetes, alcohol dependency and at least three children – one of whom has a rare genetic disorder requiring constant care – who will speak frankly about her emotional problems and sexual frustrations? And, by the way, the whole family must be identified and photographed."[15]

Annette Shaw, former PR manager of the UK No Panic self-help group, recalled: "I know about that old adage 'Never let the facts get in the way of a good story', but there are limits. We were grateful for press coverage and in my time calls to the helpline went from 100 to 1,000 per month. But I had a battle to keep the features realistic. On one occasion I was writing about OCD [obsessive compulsive disorder] for a weekly women's magazine. My case study was a professional woman, married with children… She became obsessed with numbers and checking sell-by dates. It really blighted her life, but she acknowledged the problem and wanted to tell other people like her to seek help. She agreed to be photographed, named, spoke from the heart and generally gave a good interview.

"Then the editor rang me and asked if we could spice it up by saying that as the woman lingered by the chill cabinet in Tesco's, allegedly checking her numbers, the store detectives became suspicious that she was going to put those pork chops into her pocket. I refused…One of the biggest criticisms the charity had was inaccurate portrayal by the press. Sensationalism has to have limits. If not, then case histories will be hard to find because no one will risk discussing their ailments."[16]

Insensitivity

A prominent journalist upset two couples talking about their experience of erectile dysfunction (ED) by saying she couldn't believe that a woman would be prepared to live with an impotent partner. Before photographing them the newspaper asked them to wear specific clothes and the women were given make-up. One couple felt that they were being made to look middle-class to reflect the paper's readership. Both couples wanted nothing more to do with the media.[17]

"I'm only allowing you to use your stethoscope if you promise the Daily Mail is not listening in."

It is not only journalists who can be insensitive. A couple was interviewed about ED by a doctor at a medical conference. They had a rehearsal but not with the doctor who did the final interview – when the questions were different. They felt humiliated and did not want any further conference work with doctors.

Expectations

I wrote about a woman[18] who had her first child after 19 years of waiting, ten unsuccessful IVF attempts and an £18,000 bill – a lot of money then for a carpenter and an ex-Post Office worker. Seeing her case history and baby in a national women's magazine meant a great deal to her. She saw the interview as a celebration of the most important achievement in her life, but she sensed that for me it had been "just another interview". She complained that I hadn't made her "feel special". I often think about that. Should a journalist make a subject "feel special"? Reporting on a Guild of Health Writers workshop in 2002, the late Helen Franks wrote in the Guild newsletter: "We should remember that people are giving something precious about themselves, often out of a wish to help others. A thank-you note and possibly a good gift are a good idea."[19] Some journalistic colleagues disagree.

Paying interviewees

A gift may or may not be acceptable, but what about payment? Healthcare professionals and journalists are paid for their time, so why not case-history subjects? Some delegates told the Guild workshop that they would be prepared to pay interviewees from their own fees or donate to the relevant support group or charity. But Annette Shaw said: "If money changes hands, I think the rules change. This is one of the reasons that payment for health stories is inappropriate unless to cover travel or direct expenses."[20] The same could be said of presents.

The New York Times journalism ethics policy states: "We do not pay for interviews or unpublished documents: to do so would create an incentive for sources to falsify material and would cast into doubt the genuineness of much that we publish." Bill Wheatley, then executive vice-president of the US NBC television network, said: "Any time you pay for an interview, you run the risk that the interviewee is, in effect, performing, rather than telling an honest story, to get payment."

Top of the editor's wish list

What do editors want from patient case histories? Criteria include:

- ToT – triumph over tragedy
- Beauty
- Youth
- Drama
- Celebrity

Triumph over tragedy (ToT)

The ToT formula may present subjects as super-heroes who overcome innumerable obstacles. It can have positive effects in highlighting individual achievement. For example, as a young child the supremely gifted artist Stephen Wiltshire was mute. Noting his interest in drawing, his teachers got him to speak by temporarily taking away his drawing supplies, forcing him to ask for them. He went on to art school and is now renowned all over the world for his cityscapes. Diagnosed austistic at three, he was awarded the Medal of the British Empire, one of the UK's highest honours, at the age of 32.

However, critics complain that ToT can reduce complex issues to unhelpful stereotypes that cause significant collateral damage. A story about a "heroic" cancer patient who has climbed Everest or sailed around the world may demoralise patients who struggle to climb the stairs.

Angela Wilkie, author of *Having Cancer and How to Live with It*, emphasised that her story was not how she "bravely battled" against cancer to "find true happiness". To dress up cancer with such words as "heroism" or "challenge", as the media did, she said, was to deny the pain thousands of people endure when they learn the worst.

She added: "I know there are individuals who find the experience of cancer 'productive'. There must be because I keep reading about the new enlightenment found, the benefits of a challenge met and overcome, and about the new insights into the relationship. I even read that cancer gave people their first freedom in life – the view of a popular psychiatrist. I am afraid I didn't find the two years spent battling against cancer positive in any way, least of all in my relationships with other people. In fact, I found just the opposite. My cancer was just as destructive of my personal relationships as of my health and my peace of mind… Cancer showed me things about myself and other people that I would have been far happier not knowing."[21]

The portrayal of people with disabilities might seem increasingly enlightened and a reflection of inclusiveness, but it can have unintended consequences. Media reports of the Paralympics are reported to have had a negative impact on disabled people. Speaking about the elevated status of Paralympic athletes, the disabled British presenter, actress and comedian Liz Carr explained: "There's almost the idea of the good and the bad 'cripple', and the good person is the person who is deserving, who is even more heroic. The bad is the person who's more of a burden, who's more of a drain and not really going out to achieve."[22]

Beauty
Walt Disney reportedly said: "Of all inventions for mass communication, pictures still speak the most universal language." This may be truer now than when he said it. The media have become increasingly visual. Pictures of "beautiful" people take precedence. A case history, irrespective of editorial quality, may be rejected if the editor judges any accompanying picture as "unattractive". A case history without a picture may be rejected outright. A flimsy case history may be accepted on the basis of a "good" picture. An editor may want to see a picture of the subject before commissioning a case history.

Of course, some pictures are selected for reasons other than beauty. A British journalist unable to find people willing to show the world their cellulite ended up exposing her own bottom to the camera.

Youth
The media are ageist. Perhaps, again, this is not so much a reflection of the media as of society at large. My friend David Loshak, formerly of *The Daily Telegraph* in London, assumed that his *Telegraph* retirement guide would sell well because of the paper's ageing readership. But people do not like facing up to ageing. Not for nothing is there a vibrant splash of young faces in *Telegraph* pictures. Pictures in the UK *Saga Magazine*, which targets the over-50s, also have a quasi-youthful quality.

Age discrimination may take precedence over news values. For example, a 62-year-old man was initially reported to have been "clinically dead" after an abdominal aneurysm. Among only a recorded handful of such patients to survive, his rupture occurred, by good fortune, in hospital. This was the most extraordinary case history I have ever reported, but it was not published by the commissioning newspaper. The pictures "didn't work".

Drama
Many medical case histories reported by the media are not inherently dramatic. Indeed, some of the most invaluable are pedestrian and mundane. But a dramatic storyline can give a case history a sharp edge. What makes a dramatic storyline? Whatever an editor sees as dramatic is as good a definition as any.

Celebrity
It is said to be enormously helpful to ordinary people if a celebrity talks to the media about their experience of disease or conditions such as alcoholism or drug addiction. But, as a *Lancet* editorial said in 1995, there is a darker side to loss of confidentiality.[23] It listed a succession of celebrities whose medical histories had become public property, ranging from a princess with an eating disorder and a former President who had experienced colonic polyps, gunshot wounds and Alzheimer's disease. Presumably some if not all of them waived their right to confidentiality. But how is such consent sought? This is a critical question in the light of the experience of the close family of a former UK prime minister who came under pressure from an Alzheimer's disease group to go public. The family successfully resisted. Perhaps informed consent should be sought only after a cooling down period. Patients should also be told, as far as possible, about how their cases may be reported.

News values: the editor's wish list
News values may be equally important in determining whether or not a case history is published. [News values are also discussed under the following headings in Chapter Two: *The news business*].

Novelty

The media model focuses on extremes – for example on "first" or "last", or "best" or "worst" – sometimes at the expense of the more representative middle ground. The case history of Dr Ann McPherson in the next section illustrates the potential adverse consequences of this shift from the middle ground.

Universality

Case histories about heart disease, cancer and mental illness attract extensive media attention because these conditions are widespread, often life-threatening and produce dramatic stories. Everyone knows someone who has or who has had cancer. Arguably, other, "lesser" but nonetheless traumatic conditions are under-represented in the media.

Topicality

Topical appeal can determine whether or not the media publish a case history. Patient-run websites, in contrast, can provide extensive information via patient case histories without making concessions to topicality and other news values.

Impact

A case history about the evolution of arthritis may make compelling TV without helping patients who may be more interested in learning more about how to live with the condition than with its genesis.

Controversy

Often regarded negatively, controversy opens windows onto issues of national and international importance, and none more so than assisted dying. This is illustrated in *I'll See Myself Out, Thank You*, a series of essays covering a wide range of issues about assisted suicide, from legal and religious issues to the deeply personal experiences of patients and carers. Many of these contributions were based on newspaper contributions.[24]

The alternative case-history model

The traditional media-centred model has been challenged by web-based, patient-centred models such as heathtalkonline whose content is not determined by news values. Founded in 2001 by GP and author Dr Ann McPherson and Dr Andrew Herxheimer, founder of *The Drug and*

Therapeutics Bulletin and a clinical pharmacologist with the Cochrane Collaboration, the site was originally called DIPEx [Database of Individual Patient Experiences].

McPherson, who died in 2011, recalled: "When I was diagnosed with breast cancer, even as a GP with 25 years' experience, I remember being struck by a sudden dreaded and overwhelming sense of isolation. Though I had all the hard facts, I had no idea how it would actually affect me and I wanted to hear the stories of others who had been through the same thing. I tried a support group. It was not for me... Media stories to help newly diagnosed patients were often confined to unhelpful stereotypes. Beautiful people or people who had had terrible experiences were presented as the norm. The media did not reflect the wide range of experience of illness."[25]

DIPEx aimed to provide a video and audio database of a broad spectrum of individual patients' experiences and evidence-based information about illness and treatment options. The first challenge was how to collect these experiences. A questionnaire only elicited information of the "patient satisfaction" variety rather than about the whole experience. Ticking the boxes was easy, but many respondents found writing about their conditions challenging. This problem was overcome by video and audio-recording. [Note: Chapter Eleven, *Narrative medicine* features patients who have benefited from writing about their experience of illness.]

Within ten years healthtalkonline featured almost 2,000 case histories covering cancers, heart disease, living with dying, women's health, men's health etc. It is now also used for teaching medical students and healthcare professionals about patient perspectives.

In conclusion, although charity and patient group websites have given patients a new collective voice, the consumer media are still predominant, and are likely to remain so for the foreseeable future. Journalists, including editors, as well as patients need to be educated to make the most of case histories, one of the most invaluable of all resources in medical and patient education.

SUMMARY

- Patients need to be made more aware of the potential hazards of working with the media.
- What happens when people meet journalists may be exactly the opposite of what would be expected. Impetuosity and trust may eclipse wariness and caution.
- Patient groups can now bypass the straitjacket of the news-values culture and publicise case histories on their own websites while maintaining full editiorial control.
- Such stories tend to put more emphasis on practical problems than those in traditional media.
- Individual case histories resonate more with media audiences than statistics that tend to encourage analytical thinking, to blunt emotions and turn people off. This is why charities invite donors to sponsor individual children and why the media focus on individual case histories.
- Good case histories blend the objective knowledge of medical science with the patient's subjective experience.
- Editors have a bias towards youth and beauty; the most extraordinary case histories may never be published if the pictures "don't work".

NOTES AND REFERENCES

1   Donnelly W (1997) The language of medical case histories *Annals of Internal Medicine* 127 no 11 1045-1048

2   I am not the first to have made such an observation. See Malcolm J (1990) *The Journalist and the Murderer* Alfred A. Knopf/Random House

3   Guild of Health Writers (2002) Case study workshop *Newsletter* May 21

4   Sinclair C, Makin J (2008) Medicine and the media. Sometimes it takes a loss to make a difference *BMJ* 336 73

5   Ibid

6   Small D, Loewenstein G, Slovic P (2007) Can insight breed callousness? The impact of deliberative thought on donations to identifiable and statistical victims *Organizational Behaviour and Decision Processes* 102 (2) 143-153

7   Cassidy J (2008) The soap opera that saves lives *BMJ* 336 1102

8   Williams T (1944) from the *The Glass Menagerie*

9   Bonser T (2011) He died where he wanted to *BBC Radio Four*. Friday, July 1. 08:42

10   Taman A (2011) Health in the headlines. Speaker. University of Coventry, UK. June 23-24

11   Gillie O (2011) Health in the headlines. Speaker. As ref. 10

12   Leiberman T (2011) Health in the headlines. Speaker. As ref. 10

13   Leiberman T (2007) The epidemic *Columbia Journalism Review* March-April

14   Tallis R (2008) Anecdotes, data and the curse of the media case study *HealthWatch* No.68 4-5

15   Guild of Health Writers (2002) Case study workshop *Guild Newsletter* May 21

16   Shaw A (2002) Thoughts on case studies *Guild of Health Writers Newsletter* Summer

17   Tailor A (2007) email correspondence between AT and JI

18   Illman J (1989) My baby cost me £18,000. *Woman* October 21.

19   Franks H (2002) Thoughts on Case Studies *Guild of Health Writers Newsletter* Summer

20   Shaw A (2002) Thoughts on Case Studies *Guild of Health Writers Newsletter* Summer

21   Wilkie A (1993) Interview with JI in *The Guardian* about her book *Having Cancer and How to Live with it* (1993) Hodder and Stoughton May 18.

22   Carr L (2015) Personal communication with JI.

23   Anon (1995) Celebrity illness *The Lancet* 346 517

24   *I'll See Myself Out, Thank You* (2015) edited by Colin Brewer and Michael Irwin. Skyscraper

25   McPherson A (2008) Patients' stories – entertainment or education? Address to Medical Journalists' Association, May 1.

Chapter 11

Narrative medicine. [1] Keep taking the words [2]

Read this chapter to find out about:

WRITING ABOUT PERSONAL EXPERIENCE OF ILLNESS

THERAPEUTIC WRITING

THE VISUAL DIMENSION

COMIC-BOOK MEDICINE

The central theme of this chapter has already been partly covered in Chapter Eight: *Social media and blogging*. This describes, for example, the campaign by Kate Granger, a doctor with terminal cancer, to improve communication between healthcare professionals and patients. This chapter is more about how patients use writing to manage and understand their own illnesses and to reach out to readers.

Celebrated for his sharp and witty writing, the British journalist John Diamond chronicled his long and painful experience of squamous cell carcinoma.[3] Like many other patients he saw writing as a coping mechanism.[4] His first column about his illness, in *The Times* of London, attracted hundreds of letters. The column became a regular update on his health and disease.[5] Diamond even allowed TV cameras to record his glossectomy [removal of all or part of the tongue]. The camera, he recalled, helped him to maintain his "phoney stoicism" and made it seem inappropriate to ask the "scaredy-cat questions" he wanted to ask such as "Will I live?"[6] He died in 2001.

In her memoir, *Giving up the Ghost*,[7] the novelist Hilary Mantel, twice winner of the ManBooker Prize, describes writing as a means of taking charge and even talks about writing herself "into being". Diagnosed with endometriosis at the age of 27, she gained weight after hormone treatment and felt "mauled" by medical procedures.

Kay Redfield Jamison, author of *An Unquiet Mind: A memoir of moods and madness*[8] and a professor of psychiatry at John Hopkins University School of Medicine, Baltimore, Maryland, was understandably wary of writing about her own manic depressive illness. But it seems to have had a strong liberating effect – to have brought her out of hiding, enabling her to talk freely and frankly about her condition. The benefits, of course, are palliative, not curative, and not without adverse effects. For example, she has had to balance her belief that "what is personal should stay personal" with her position as a widely published writer, academic and mental-health crusader. She has had worries that peers may see her more as a subjective patient than as an independent academic – she is a world authority on mood disorders. The status of manic depressive illness as a genetic disease is another preoccupation. "Write about what you know" can be good advice, but writing about something that may impact on family or friends needs careful consideration. [Writing about who you know, as many others do, is something else again.]

Lewis Wolpert, emeritus professor in cell and developmental biology, University College London, and author of *Malignant Sadness: The Anatomy of Depression*,[9] has also spoken about his decision to write openly about his illness. Any idea that it is courageous, he says, is evidence that the stigma of mental illness is still alive and well. Feeling completely shameless about his condition he cites four reasons for writing about it: to help those living or working with sufferers to understand depression; to help sufferers to understand themselves; to remove the stigma of depression, and, foremost, to try to understand it in scientific terms.

Adrian Sudbury, web editor of the British *Huddersfield Daily Examiner*, developed acute myeloid leukaemia in his twenties. Like many journalists he had a compulsive urge to write and began blogging when he was unable to contribute to the paper. "Baldy's blog", he said, was also a means of giving something back to his supportive colleagues and employers.

He wrote: "Anyone reading this will probably agree, if they are honest, that with a few notable exceptions, the majority of blogs are dreadful – so I feel there is a certain irony that I should finish up writing one. It was for that reason… I didn't begin writing a blog sooner. My concern was that it would become too self-indulgent. Does anyone really want to read about someone struggling with cancer? But as the treatment progressed, you find you have days when you feel well enough to write…I convinced myself that leukaemia and the unpleasant problems that go with it might be of interest to a wider audience.

"I know my blog won't change anything or stop anyone else developing the disease. But if any good does come from it, I hope it helps in some small way to clear up the general confusion surrounding bone marrow donations and transplants. There's no medieval equipment involved, and, for most donors, donating bone marrow is actually not too different from giving blood."[10]

Sudbury died in 2008 after attracting an international following and being commended by the then UK Prime Minister, Gordon Brown.

Writing as therapy – but not for publication

Therapeutic writing may also help people who do not write for publication. This area is beyond but allied to this book's remit. Dr Gillie Bolton, author of *The Therapeutic Potential of Creative Writing: Writing Myself,*[11] believes that writing saved her sanity after trauma in her early 30s. Responding to her husband's suggestion that she should write an autobiography, she wrote "a lovely glorious story" and then produced "something far more chaotic but closer to the truth". She then refined it again, this time into poetry.

Experience taught that it was not just the first cathartic outpouring that mattered, but the redrafting. This helped her to understand what had happened to her. She didn't seek conventional therapy because she couldn't trust a therapist the way she could a piece of paper. "Paper's always there to re-read or rewrite," she explained. "Once you've said something, you can't unsay it, but with a page of writing you can. You don't ever have to share it. You can burn it if you want."

Formerly a senior research fellow in medicine and the arts at King's College London, Bolton uses therapeutic writing in reflective practice seminars with healthcare professionals.[12] "We use it to explore work issues, relationships with colleagues and the like. A lot of people say, after writing something, they could never have told me without writing it first. I sometimes ask doctors to write in the voice of a patient. They find this illuminating. The value of doing this is hard to overestimate, from their future patients' point of view and their own."

Bolton and Sheffield GP David Gelipter maintain that studying literature and practising writing can engender rounded understandings and skills essential to doctors.[13] Understanding and learning about other people's lives habitually happens in story form, particularly, she says, in medicine. "Patients bring narratives; clinicians create them and help patients rewrite theirs."

Picture-book medicine

"Patient-story" blogs and books tend to be heavy on words and light on pictures. In what may be the first such book, Keith Hern closed the gap with 34 pictures in *Bangers and Mash,*[14] an account of his experience of throat cancer. A British professional photographer, Hern believes that *seeing*, say, pictures of a radiotherapy machine or chemotherapy equipment can reduce pre-treatment anxiety, preventing a patient's imagination from running riot. Just reading about such procedures, he says, may not have the same impact. Before and after pictures of his surgical scarring and hair loss have also reduced fear among readers, he says. The illustrations include six pictures charting the making of his plaster-of-Paris radiotherapy mask. The more comprehensive the overall visual picture, Hern believes, the less the risk of anxiety.

Comic-book medicine

Millions of children are diagnosed with conditions they may not understand. Children are often said to be too young to comprehend medical concepts, or worse, to be better off not knowing. This may actually exacerbate their problems. Kindergarten children typically understand the cause of illnesses as "quite magical" and/or as the result of their transgression of the rules.[15] They may think, for example, that "the demon in their belly" is a punishment.[16]

Responding to the lack of engaging, educative information for their young patients, Drs Kim Chilman-Blair and Kate Hersov founded Medikidz in 2009.[17] The company develops comic books about paediatric conditions ranging from epilepsy to scoliosis and from leukaemia to cystic fibrosis. It has distributed more than 3,500,000 comic books globally. Based on a real-life case, each title takes about five months to produce. The books are written by the Medikidz medical team of doctors and are externally peer reviewed by leading experts. Children, especially the source, are consulted throughout the production process.

The Medikidz, five larger-than-life super-heroes from outer space, specialise in different parts of the body and live on Mediland, a planet shaped like the human body. Axon is the brain specialist; Pump has the lowdown on heart and blood vessels; Chi knows all about lungs; Skinderella, about skin and bone; and Gastro, about "your tum, bottom and all the tubes in between".

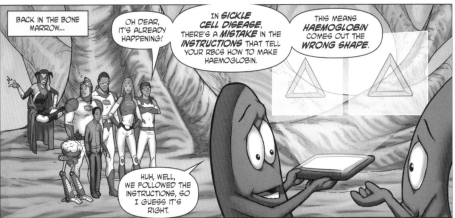

Photo credit: *Medikidz*
Comic book strips about the body can help to engage children and help them to understand illness.
Medikidz has developed comic books about paediatric conditions ranging from cystic fibrosis to leukaemia.
It has distributed more than 3,500,000 comic books globally.

Hersov says: "With children it's all about engagement. Without engagement it's difficult to educate." Six story-line ingredients have been found to contribute to success:[18]

- Immediate engagement
- Analogies/metaphors
- Characters
- Explanation of complex issues
- Heroes/heroines
- Humour

It's not just children who need to be "engaged". Everyone you communicate with in a media interview or in a presentation or a piece of writing needs to be engaged. This is a recurring theme in this book. Hersov also flags up the advantage of using analogies and metaphors in communicating with children. Again, this is just as important with adults. In addition, characters [case histories] and storytelling are as important in adult media communication as they are in comic books. Speakers who tell a good story, like the story itself, tend to be remembered.

SUMMARY

- People use writing as a means of managing and understanding their illnesses. One prominent novelist sees writing as a means of "taking charge".
- So called therapeutic writing may help people who do not want to write for publication.
- Seeing pictures of, say, a radiotherapy machine or chemotherapy equipment may reduce pre-treatment anxiety, preventing patients' imagination from running riot, according to a professional photographer who has produced a picture book documenting his experience of treatment for throat cancer.
- Medical comic books provide engaging, educative information for young patients.

NOTES AND REFERENCES

1   The term "narrative medicine" has evolved from work by physicians such as Naiomi Remen and Rita Charon who advocate structuring medical practice around a narrative. See Greenhalgh T, Huritz B (1999) Narrative-based medicine. Why study narrative? *BMJ* 318: 48-50 http://www.bmj.com/cgi/content/full/318/7175/48

2   "Keep taking the words" is taken from *Write Yourself: Creative Writing and Personal Development* by Gillie Bolton (2011) Jessica Kingsley

3   John Diamond was the author of C: *Because Cowards Get Cancer Too* Vermilion (1999)

4   Anon. *Daily Telegraph* (2001) Obituary. March 3, 2001

5   Preston J (2001) A man of many notes. Obituary. *Sunday Telegraph* March 4. April 19. Books. Cover story.

6   Anon. *Daily Telegraph* (2001) Obituary. March 3

7   Mantel H (2003) *Giving Up the Ghost* Fourth Estate

8   Redfield Jamison K (1995) *An Unquiet Mind. A memoir of moods and madness* Picador

9   Wolpert L (1999) *Malignant Sadness: The Anatomy of Depression* Faber and Faber

10 Sudbury A (2007) Baldy's Blog. *Huddersfield Daily Examiner*. These excerpts were also reported by *UK Press Gazette* under the headline Reporting from the edge: web editor's leukaemia blog. p 15. May 18. http://boldlyblog.freshblogs.co.uk

11 Bolton G (1998) *Therapeutic Potential of Creative Writing: Writing Myself* Jessica Kingsley

12 www.gilliebolton.com

13 Ibid

14 Hern K (2009) *Bangers and Mash* MX Publishing

15 Perrin EC, Gerrity PS (1980) There's a demon in your belly: Children's understanding of Illness. *Pediatrics* 67 841

16 Ibid

17 www.medikidz.com

18 HPI (2011) Medikidz research – graphic novels evaluation development with children

Chapter 12

Medicine and the media: 1950-2000. A brief history

This chapter is about ten developments that changed the doctor-patient relationship – and in turn the relationship between medicine and the media.

Technological development

The 1950s radiated the change of postwar optimism and dazzling scientific and technological innovation in medicine, atomic energy and space exploration. The Sputnik space launch (1957) generated unprecedented global excitement. Medical technology and the space programme shared the dreams of a high-tech future.[1] In a classic example of journalistic reaction to the new and exciting, more and more journalists specialised in medical and scientific reporting.

Education

Explosive growth in higher education created many more graduates than industry could absorb, encouraging expansion of the social sciences and humanities and a general backlash against the professions. Until the 1960s most sociologists perceived medicine as a profession that acted in a rational and benevolent way. The growth of a "more critical sociology encouraged an alternative view of medicine as a dominating profession that medicalised everyday life".[2]

This was part of a general trend – the revolt of the "Swinging Sixties", symbolised by The Rolling Stones, The Beatles, student uprising, the Civil Rights Movement, the Campaign for Nuclear Disarmament, the Vietnam War movement, women's liberation, satire and the advent of the contraceptive pill, a driver of sexual revolution. Nothing was sacred any more.

"We told the architect to make transparency a priority."

Consumerism

On March 15,1962, US President John F Kennedy outlined his vision of consumer rights. The first politician to set out such principles formally, he stated that consumers had the right to:

- Safety
- Be informed
- Choose
- Be heard

Consumerism was slow to embrace healthcare, but campaigners subsequently presented it as a means of addressing "the present imbalance between medical professionals and their patients. The former have power, the latter do not."[3] Was this fair comment or an unjustified attack against medicine? Information for patients in the 1950s and 1960s was in short supply. It now seems remarkable that in the UK medications were labelled mysteriously "The mixture" or "The tonic". Hospital records were stamped "Confidential: not to be seen by the patient". [Such records were still in use in the 1980s.]

Some professionals assumed that too much information, especially about side effects, caused anxiety. But the reverse was found to be true. For example, the more information surgical patients had, the less likely they were to have post-operative complications. In radiotherapy greater knowledge about the treatment was associated with less emotional distress. Studies such as these increased the demand for transparency that most people, only 30 or so years later, take for granted. I know that such research would have shocked a dedicated, older physician who complained to me around 1990 that the "architecture of transparency" was stripping medicine of its power at the expense of patients. His was not a lone voice.

The Women's Liberation Movement

The WLM insisted that women had the right to know and decide about medical procedures that affected their bodies and their lives. The US Boston Women's Health Collective, in effect, wrote in *Our Bodies Ourselves: a Health Book by and for Women,* a health manifesto for the 21st century.[4] Its major emphasis was on personal responsibility in healthcare. Most western governments now emphasise the need for personal responsibility in prevention of illness and for greater voluntary involvement in healthcare. One controversial feminist view was that detailed information about healthcare had been akin to a form of contraband smuggled through the underground press or by word of mouth.[5]

The WLM's call for personal responsibility for health ignited debate about the so-called "expert patient", "the informed patient" and "the doctor-patient partnership" in which doctor and patient decided what to do for the best. Of course, these were and are models, broad sweeps of the brush. As doctors and patients we play many different roles. It is easy to be a proactive patient if you are fit and well and are having a routine check. Many a cancer patient is grateful for an old-fashioned dose of paternalism. But paternalism was rationed in the name of political correctness. For right or wrong, "Patient Power" became the new war cry.

The self-help movement

Self-help, the fastest-growing part of the human services industry, which burgeoned in the 1960s and 1970s, was reported to reflect disillusionment with the established helping services, a wave of anti-professionalism, changing ideas about what medicine could actually achieve,[6] and a growing realisation that caring professionals could never provide the amount of personal, sustained engagement many patients felt they needed.[7]

Media coverage of personal case histories in the UK uncovered the depth of public desire for mutual help and support, encouraging the formation of a myriad of support groups such as the Parkinson's Disease Society. Mali Jenkins founded the society [now Parkinson's UK]. Cared for by the family, her sister Sarah had been living with the condition for some years. Frustrated to find no literature in layman's terms about the condition, Mali placed adverts in the personal columns of newspapers appealing for people who were interested in forming an exploratory group. Sixteen people attended the first meeting in 1969. Mali chaired the committee and her sister Eryl was the secretary. Other members of the family and friends also helped. Parkinson's UK now has 365 local groups.

Such groups were often overwhelmed by public response.[8] This new brand of self-help and consumerism gave millions of patients a collective voice for the first time, setting the stage for the internet revolution 30 years later.

Self-help groups generated a rich seam of media medical case histories –
people-based stories sell. This was the foundation for consumer health and
medical journalism as we know it today.

Thalidomide

Mothers in 46 countries around the world took thalidomide, a mild
sedative and morning sickness treatment. Allegedly "non toxic" and "safe"
even for pregnant women, it deformed 8,000 babies.[9] Some had no arms,
just hands from the shoulder; some no legs, just toes from their hips; some
had limbless trunks, with just a head and a body.[10]

The story first hit the headlines in the German *Welt am Sonntag* newspaper
in 1961, shaking public faith in modern medicines and prescribers.
Thalidomide changed the relationship between medicine and the media,
even though the thrust of media scrutiny was directed not so much against
prescribers as manufacturers. Doctors, for so long a race apart, were no
longer off limits.

Thalidomide also challenged the assumption that non-medically trained
journalists could not report complex medical issues. Thalidomide was to
medical journalism what Watergate would be to politics. For a decade *The
Sunday Times* battled against Distillers, culminating in 1979 with the
300-page *Suffer The Children: The Story of Thalidomide*. Medicine and
Big Pharma had never before been exposed to such intense journalistic
attention, despite indignation against the press for prying into affairs that
did not concern it.[11]

Could *The Sunday Times* break a thalidomide-like story today?[12] Media
companies lack resources for complex, lengthy investigations. Harold
Evans [now Sir Harold], then *The Sunday Times* editor, would have to be
extremely brave today to pay his whistleblower £8,000 for files from the
manufacturer.[13] He would also have to break the law. The UK Bribery Act
2010 makes it illegal to pay for information that may reveal corruption.

The new heavy-handedness of the law threatens not only the media.
Companies increasingly use libel law to intimidate individuals, including
healthcare professionals. British cardiologist Dr Peter Wilmshurst spent
almost four years fighting four libel actions by a US company after publicly

highlighting what he believed were fundamental flaws in the clinical trial of a device to close a hole in the heart. Wilmshurst refused to back down in the face of possible financial ruin. He was vindicated.

The world's first human-to-human heart transplant

Much of what is now routine in medical news reporting can be traced back to this operation in South Africa in 1967. It was as big a media story as man's first steps on the moon [in 1969]. Many people thought the operation either could not or should not be performed. The lead surgeon, Professor Christiaan Barnard, became the most celebrated name in medicine and surgery since Hippocrates. Relishing celebrity status, he declared that anyone who didn't like publicity must be mad.[14] Courted by the rich and famous and received by the Pope, he had an affair with Italian film star Gina Lollobrigida. Media profiles compared his boyish good looks to those of TV's *Dr Kildare* and even John F Kennedy.

More seriously, the operation prompted a new kind of medical reporting, taking in ethical and social issues as well as clinical practice,[15] and ushering in a new style of TV medical debate. Doctors were publicly *seen* to have conflicting views, a radical shift for a privately critical but publicly silent profession. The idea of being in a media controversy may seem alarming, but controversy, to repeat an earlier point, is usually more of an opportunity than a threat for the well-prepared media interviewee. Sidestepping controversy may give undue prominence to opposing views.

HIV/AIDS

The AIDS Coalition to Unleash Power [ACTUP] was possibly the most significant direct-action campaign in the US since the anti-Vietnam War movement in the 1960s,[16] and the single most important development in patients' rights in the 20th century. It became the template for thousands of advocacy groups for patients all over the world with diseases ranging from depression to breast cancer. Generating extensive media coverage through skilful public relations, the AIDS movement was highly expert, with many patients knowing as much as doctors about new treatments.

As research and development director at the Wellcome Foundation in the UK [part of GlaxoSmithKline since the merger of Glaxo Wellcome and SmithKline Beecham in 2000], Professor Trevor Jones, was responsible for developing azidothymidine [AZT], the first HIV/AIDS treatment. The research was put at risk when, for the first time, a group outside medicine and the pharmaceutical industry challenged clinical trial protocols.

Jones took the unprecedented step of inviting AIDS activists into the laboratories because trialists had been compromising studies by mixing active drugs with placebos. He recalled: "We had to do it. When the activists arrived, there was anger, but the anger was basically a *cri de coeur*. They were saying: 'Help me. I have a problem and you may or may not be able to help. But it's my life, and I want to be involved in the decisions.' That changed the way we thought about doing things. From that moment I knew we must involve patients."[17]

Medical ethics

Melanie Phillips, then of *The Guardian* in London, and the late Dr John Dawson, of the British Medical Association, wrote *Doctors' Dilemmas: Medical Ethics and Contemporary Science*.[18] It now seems extraordinary that they declared in 1985: "When a doctor and a journalist get together to write a book, eyebrows may be raised. When the subject of the book is medical ethics, one of the most difficult and sensitive areas of medicine, the eyebrows may well disappear into the hairline completely."

In the 1980s, many doctors believed that medical ethics were so intimately related to clinical judgement that the only people who could rule on it were doctors themselves. Phillips and Dawson commented: "To enlist the aid of a journalist to grapple with this most delicate of subjects would seem to many doctors incomprehensible to the point of treachery." Other external voices also protested that medicine had had it all its own way for far too long, and that it was high time for other disciplines – law, philosophy, religion and so on – to join the ethics debate.

The Internet

The media used to be *the* gatekeepers between medicine and the wider public. Patients, doctors, healthcare companies, charities and patient groups can now bypass the media and reach a global audience in seconds with a simple click of a computer mouse. There is much more I could write about this, but it is the subject of another book.

Conclusion

Media reporting about all these developments provoked allegations that the media were demonising medicine and baying for its blood, but medicine, I believe, was shooting the messenger. Newsgathering is reactive – a response to an event or development, not a witch hunt. This point is not just of academic interest. Unfounded criticism of the media, to repeat an earlier point, will discourage healthcare professionals from working with journalists. If medicine does not represent in the media it will be misrepresented. Journalists need reliable sources.

SUMMARY

- The self-help movement in the 1960s and 1970s laid the foundations for today's brand of medical journalism, with its reliance on individual case histories.
- Consumerism gave patients a new collective voice.
- The thalidomide tragedy was to medical journalism what the Watergate scandal would be to political journalism.
- In a radical shift for a privately critical but publicly silent profession, the world's first human-to-human heart transplant in 1967 encouraged a new kind of public debate, in which, perhaps for the first time, doctors were seen publicly to have conflicting views.
- The fledgling HIV/AIDS lobby was the template for tens of thousands of advocacy groups all over the world for a wide range of conditions. (Patient advocacy is what happens when self-help gets political.)
- The media used to be the gatekeepers between medicine and the wider public. Anyone using the internet can now bypass the media and reach a global audience within seconds.

NOTES AND REFERENCES

1 Natho A (2009) *Hearts Exposed. Transplants and the Media in 1960s Britain* Palgrave Macmillan p 49

2 Gabe J, Kelleher D, Williams G (1994) *Challenging Medicine* Routledge pp (Preface)

3 Young M (1983) The four purposes and the six methods *Self-Health, Jnl. of the College of Health* No 1 p 3

4 Ibid p 11

5 Ehrenreich B (1984) The body politic p 52. *MS* magazine May

6 Robinson D, Henry S (1977) *Self-Health and Health: Mutual Aid for Modern Problems* p 11 Martin Robertson

7 Robinson D, Robinson Y (1979) *From Self-help to Health* p 7 Concord Books

8 Robinson D, Henry S (1977) *Self-Help and Health: Mutual Aid for Modern Problems* p 21-22 Martin Robertson

9 *Sunday Times* Insight Team (1979) *Suffer the Children: The Story of Thalidomide* Andre Deutsch

10 Ibid p 1

11 Ibid p 4

12 Cavendish C (2012) Could the press expose thalidomide today? *The Times* Jan. 19. p 23

13 Evans H (2009) *My Paper Chase: True Stories of Vanished Times* Little, Brown. Cited by Cavendish C: ref 20

14 Munnion C (2001) Pioneer who became a playboy seduced by fame *Daily Telegraph* Sept 3

15 Nathoo A (2009) *Hearts Exposed: Transplants and the Media in 1960s Britain* p 186 Palgrave Macmillan

16 Watney S (1994) Foreword to *Reports from the Holocaust: The Making of an Aids Activist* by Larry Kramer. Cassell

17 Illman J (2000) *The Expert Patient* pp 12-13 ABPI

18 Phillips M, Dawson J (1985) Preface to *Doctors' Dilemmas: Medical Ethics and Contemporary Science* Harvester Press

Epilogue

Just before the 2015 Paris terrorist attacks I emailed 20 friends and colleagues a possible front-cover logo for this book. It comprised a stethoscope suspended around a TV transmitter tower,. The idea was to symbolise medicine and the media. I did not explain it. I just asked my random sample what it meant to them. It was interpreted, among many other things, as the Eiffel Tower and the possible strangulation of France by so-called Islamic State.

I had assumed it would be easily understood – as it might have been before the bombers and gunmen struck. Good communication is about being understood. Great communication is about not being misunderstood and meeting the Einstein challenge – making things as simple as possible but no simpler. Testing messages and images can help to avoid possible ambiguity.

I want to make one more point about picture power by expressing my admiration for cartoonists who can tell a story in three or four words and just a few lines and strokes. This is an exacting discipline. Visualising a story as they do can help to clarify it, reducing it to bare essentials, enabling you to say as little as possible but as much as necessary to meet your goal.

Finally: a request. A reporter's involvement with a story usually used to end when it went to the editor. This is no longer so. Submitting a story may be just the beginning of a reporter's relationship with it. For example, Twitter generates extensive debate about news, precipitating follow-up stories and yet more debate. I hope that the same will be true of this book. Please email me [john@jicmedia.co.uk] with questions, comments and observations of interest to fellow readers. I would like to blog about such material and perhaps include it in future editions. Thank you for reading the first edition.

Further reading

Some of the books below are more than 20 years old – a long time in an era of unprecedented change. Some lack information that is now considered basic. For example, Tim Albert's *Medical Journalism: the writer's guide* (1992) includes minimal reference to evidence-based medicine, statistics and clinical trials, but many of the chapters – for example, *Understanding the writer* are as relevant now as when they were written.

Media interviews and presentation

John Adair (1997) *Effective Communication (The Most Important Management Tool of All)* PAN BOOKS

Michael Bland (1998) *Communicating out of a Crisis* MACMILLAN BUSINESS

John Clare (2012) *Communicating Clearly about Science and Medicine* GOWER

Chip Heath and Dan Heath (2008) *Made to Stick: Why some ideas take hold and others come unstuck* ARROW BOOKS

William Hawes (1991) *Television Performing: News and Information* FOCAL PRESS

Jacey Lamerton (2001) *Public Speaking: Speak in Public with Confidence* HARPERCOLLINS

Garr Reynolds (2008) *Presentation Zen: Simple Ideas on Presentation, Design and Delivery* NEW RIDERS

Chris Rose (2005) *How to Win Campaigns: 100 steps to success* EARTHSCAN

John B Lidstone (1992) *Face the Press: Managing the media interview* NICHOLAS BREALEY PUBLISHING

Stephen White, Peter Evans, Chris Mihill, Maryon Tysoe (1993) *Hitting the Headlines: a practical guide to the media* BRITISH PSYCHOLOGICAL SOCIETY

Journalism

Harold Evans (2009) *My Paper Chase: True Stories of Vanished Times* LITTLE, BROWN AND COMPANY.

Alexander Kendrick (1969) *The Life of Edward R Murrow* LITTLE, BROWN AND COMPANY.

Andrew Marr (2004) *My Trade. A Short History of British Journalism* MACMILLAN

John Sergeant (2001) *Give Me Ten Seconds* MACMILLAN

Medical journalism and writing

Tim Albert (1992) *Medical Journalism: the Writer's Guide.* RADCLIFFE MEDICAL PRESS

Tim Albert (2000) *A-Z of Medical Writing* BMJ BOOKS

Tammy Boyce (2007) *Health, Risk and News: The MMR Vaccine and the Media* PETER LANG

Ben Goldacre (2009) *Bad Science* FOURTH ESTATE.

Neville W Goodman and Martin B Edwards (1991) *Medical Writing: a Prescription for Clarity – a self-help guide to clearer medical English* CAMBRIDGE UNIVERSITY PRESS

Brendan Hennessy (1993) *Writing Feature Articles: A practical guide to methods and markets Articles* FOCAL PRESS

Ragnar Levi (2001) *Medical Journalism: Exposing Fact, Fiction* FRAUD JOHN WILEY

John Lister [author, editor] (2014) *First Do No Harm: Reporting on Health and Health Care* LIBRI PUBLISHING

Ayesha Nathoo A (2009) *Hearts Exposed: Transplants and the Media in 1960s Britain* PALGRAVE MACMILLAN

Peter Richardson [editor] (2002) *A Guide to Medical Publishing and Writing: Your Questions Answered* (2002) QUAY BOOKS DIVISION, MARK ALLEN PUBLISHING

Richard Smith (2006) *The Trouble with Medical Journals* ROYAL SOCIETY OF MEDICINE PRESS

Sunday Times Insight Team (1979) *Suffer the Children. The Story of Thalidomide* ANDRE DEUTSCH

Tony Thistlethwaite (1997) *Independent and Bloody Minded: The Story of the Medical Journalists' Association: 1967-97* MEDICAL JOURNALISTS ASSOCIATION

Social media

Nicholas Carr (2010) *The Shallows: How the Internet is Changing the Way We Think, Read and Remember* ATLANTIC BOOKS

Kevin Pho and Susan Gay (2013) *Establishing, Managing and Protecting Your Online Reputation: A Social Media*

Guide for Physicians and Medical Practices GREENBRANCH PUBLISHING

Tim O'Reilly and Sarah Milstein (2009) *The Twitter Book* O'REILLY

Writing for the media

Sally Adams with Wynford Hicks (2001) *Interviewing for journalists* ROUTLEDGE

The Associated Press Stylebook, 2015. ASSOCIATED PRESS.

Guardian and Observer style guide. THE GUARDIAN. Available free on line

Harold Evans (2000) *Essential English for Journalists, Editors and Writers* PIMLICO. REVISED BY CRAWFORD GILLAN

John Humphrys (2004) *Lost for Words: The Mangling and Manipulating of the English Language* HODDER AND STOUGHTON

David Marsh (2013) *For Who the Bell Tolls: the essential and entertaining guide to grammar* GUARDIAN BOOKS AND FABER AND FABER

Rick Thompson (2005) *Writing for Broadcast Journalists* ROUTLEDGE

Mark Stuart [editor] (2007) *The Complete Guide to Medical Writing* PHARMACEUTICAL PRESS

In addition

Stuart Allan (2002) *Media, Risk and Science (Issues in Culture and Media Studies)* OPEN UNIVERSITY PRESS. Includes a sweep of the media's handling of topics such as environmental risk, HIV/AIDS, food scares and human cloning.

Gillie Bolton (1998) *Therapeutic Potential of Creative Writing: Writing Myself* JESSICA KINGSLEY PUBLISHERS. Using writing to make sense of experience and to promote self-understanding.

Mark Henderson (2012) *The Geek Manifesto: Why science matters* BANTAM PRESS. A "must" read for anyone interested in science communication in the internet age.

Richard Horton (2004) *MMR Science and Fiction: Exploring the Vaccine Crisis* GRANTA PUBLICATIONS. An insider's view by *The Lancet* editor. The journal published and later retracted the work by Dr Andrew Wakefield and 11 others that caused the crisis.

Index

A

ACTUP 176
Adams, Sally 78 90
Alcohol 88
Altman, Doug 25
American Association for the Advancement of Science 96
American Hospital Association 152
Anti-vaccination lobby 33 47 56-57
Anxiety 72 94 113 140
Arnold, Matthew 104
Attributable [interviews] 42

B

Balance [news reporting] 24-26
Barnard Christian 8 176
Barrington Brown, Anthony 35 38
BBC 24 40 81 84 87
Berry, Cicely 90 136 145
Bipolar disorder 61 67
Birmingham Children's Hospital 151
Blogging: creating a blog,115; naming your blog, 116-117; developing ideas and post titles, 117-118; search engine optimisation [SEO], 118; the novice's dilemma, 120; frequency of posts, 121. State of art blogs 115-116 120-121
Blonstein, Joseph 19
BMJ 82 90 98 108 121 128 131 149 151 162 170
Body language 72 74-75 82 138-140
Bolsin, Steve 48
Bolton, Gillie 166 170
Bongi [blogger] 120
Bonser, Tony 151 162
Bowel cancer 29 32 44 150
Bradford Hill, Austin 29 36 38 97 108
Brady, John 76 90
Breakfast news 81
Brown, Gordon 165

C

Calacanis, Jason 70
Calman, Kenneth 36 38
Cameron, David 110
Carr, Liz 157 182
Case histories [media] 147-162
Chalmers, Iain Sir 25 27
Channel 4 86
Chilman-Blair, Kim 167
Cochrane Collaboration 160

Columbia Journalism Review 152
Comic book medicine [children] 167-169
Conan Doyle, Arthur 92
Consumerism 14 173 174 178
Coolidge, Calvin 107
Cooper, Carol 22 27 97 108
Covey, Stephen 64 131 145
Creasy, Stella 125
Crick, Francis 35
Crichton, Michael 92
Crisis management 47
Cronin, Archibald [AJ] 92
Curry, Stephen [Reciprocal Space blog] 120 127
Consumerism 14 173-174 178

D

Dacre, Paul 29
Dahl, R 33 38 57 60 62 64
Daily Mail 8 22 29 30 34 38
Daily Telegraph 157 170 179
Daniels, Ron 113-114 119
Davis, Evan 123
Dawson, John 177 179
Deadlines 42 71 72 104
Defamation 124-125
Department of Health [UK] 36
Diamond, John 13 164 170
DIPEX: healthtalkonline 160
DISCERN 100
Disney, Walt 157
Doll, Richard Sir 29 36 38 97
Donnelly, William 147 162
Dr Wes [blog] 115-116

E

Ebbinghaus, Hermann 63 64
English, David Sir 30
Einstein, Albert 55 181
Ernst, Edzard 24 93-94 103 108
Ethics 131 149 151 155 177 179
Evans, Harold [Harry] Sir 29 175 179

F

Facebook 114-115 124 128 148
Ferriman, Annabel 20 27 50 52
Fiske, Peter 131 145
Fly-on-the-wall documentaries 86-87 90
"Forgetting curve" 63
Franks, Helen 155 162

G

Gabbay, Mark 86-87 90
Gelipter, David 166
Gettysburg Address 105 108
Gillie, Oliver 152 162
Glasziou, Paul 25 27
GlaxoSmithKline 176
Google 32 96 115 117 119
Granger, Kate 110-112 113 116 123 126
Grayling, Chris 24
Greenslade, Roy 17 27
Guardian, The 27 32 38 50 72 97 106 118 120
    127 162 177
Guild of Health Writers 149 155 162
Gwande, Atul 135-36

H

Hate mail 93
Health News Review 20 100-101
Health scares 46-47
Health Service Journal 113 127
Heart transplant [first] 176
Hern, Keith 166 170
Hersoz, Kate 167
Herxheimer, Andrew 159
HIV/AIDS 176-177 178
Holt, Kim 49
Hunt, Jeremy 110

I

Ideas: [writing] developing, 94-97 117-118; sub-
    mitting/pitching ideas, 97-98; also see writing
IMRAD 97
Interviews: responding to requests, 39-47;
    defining objectives, 55; developing messages,
    55-60; anticipating questions, 60-62; different
    interview formats, 65-72; telephone; 41 62 75-76;
    recording [telephone] 76 78-79; radio, 81-84; TV,
    84-90; pre-recorded broadcast interviews, 88;
    previewing copy/stories, 79-80; dress and rules
    of engagement; [for interviewers] 103; "doorstep"
    interviews, 78; whistleblowing, 47-49

J

Jargon 104 142
Jenkins, Simon 120
Johannsson, Helgi 112-113
Jones, Trevor 176
Journalism: different types of journalist, 17-19;
    medical journalists, 19-23; balance in, 24-26;
    news values, 31-37.

K

Kennedy, John F 38 176
Kinnock, Neil 80 90
Kipling, Rudyard 40 60 64

L

Lancet, The 26 27 31 50 98 158 162
Law 25 76 124-127 175 177
Larsson, Anna 21 27
Lennane, Jean 49
Less is More Medicine [blog] 115-116
Lieberman, Trudi 152
Levi, Ragnar 19 27
Libel 124-125
Lincoln, Abraham 105 108
LinkedIn 115
Loshak, David 157

M

Mangold, Tom 40
Mantel, Hilary 13 164 170
Marciano, Sally-Ann 113-114
McAlpine, Lord 124-125 127
McPherson, Ann 99-100 108 159-160 162
Mawdsley, Anne 79 90
Medicine-media relationship 23
Medical journalists 18-24
Medikidz 167-169
MMR vaccine 33 38 57
Mendoza, Nancy 131 145
Messages [developing] 55-60
Molnar, Frank 99 108
Morris, Desmond 57 64
Mother Teresa, of Calcutta 150
Munger, Dave 119 127
Myspace 124

N

Newhart, Bob 40 52
News agenda 34 37 50
News values 26 31-37 59 148 156-159
Non-attributable 42
Nursing Times 113 127

O

Observer, The 50 79-80 90 93
Oliver, Clare 149 150 153
O'Donnell, Michael 23 30
On/off the record 42
O'Riordan, Dermot 113
Oransky, Ivan 21 27

Ornstein, Charles 23 27
Orwell, George 104-105
Osler, William 134

P
Parkin, Beverley 30-31 38
Phillips, Melanie 177 179
Pho, Kevin 114 128
Photographers 78
Pictures; [for radio] 84; [age discrimination in
    media] 157-158
"Picture book medicine" 166-167
Pitching [idea] 98 [talk] 132
Potter, Dennis 32 45 52
Powell, Enoch 19
Press conferences 80-81
Press officers 12 52 77
Press releases 49-50 52 96 101
Psychiatric Bulletin 30 38

R
Radio cars 77
Raynaud's and Scleroderma Association, UK 79 90
Reagan, Ronald 29 32 38 44 52
Redfield Jamison, Kay 164 170
Reid, Andrew 124-125
Reynolds, Garr 144 145
Roddy, Elin 112
Rosenberg, Scott 70
Rosenheim, Lord 74
Rosling, Hans 141
Royal College of General Practitioners 117 125 128
Royal College of Nursing 34
Royal College of Physicians of Edinburgh 16
Royal Free Hospital, London 33
Royal Pharmaceutical Society 31

S
Saga Magazine 157
Sagan, Carl 25
Schwitzer, Gary 19 20-21 27 100-101
Self-help 47 131 153 174 178 179
Shaw, Annette 153 155 162
Singing Detective, The 32 45 52
SmithKline Beecham 176
Smith, Michael 82
Smoking 29 36 38
Social media: uses, 110-114; platforms, 114-115;
    Social Media Highway Code 125 128

Somerset Maugham, William 92
Soul City 150-151 153 162
Strobing 89
Sudbury, Adrian 165 170
Sunday Times, The 25 27 29 152 175 179 181

T
Talks: active-passive voice, 131; planning, 131-135;
    voice, 136; body language, 138-140; anxiety, 140;
    Visual aids, 140-141; slide use, 141-144; question
    time, 144-145
Tallis, Raymond 152 162
Taman, Alan 151-152 162
TED Talks 145
Thalidomide 14 175 178 179
Thatcher, Margaret 57 64 125
Therapeutic writing 13-14 166 169
Thistlethwaite, Tony 27
Time magazine 35
Times, The 31 35 38 50 97 120 164 179
Todorov, Alexander 74 90
Tomalin, Nicholas 17 27
Transplants 14 21 31-32 33 34 96 165 176 178 179

V
Vogelstein, Fred 70

W
Wakefield, Andrew 33
Walker, Isabel 22 27
Watson, James 35
West, Fred 32-33
Whistleblowing 47-49
Wilkes, Eric 57
Wilkie, Angela 156 162
Willis, Janine 74 90
Wiltshire, Stephen 156
Winer, Dave 70
Wing of Zock [blog] 115
Winston, Lord 45 52
Wolpert, Lewis 165 170
Women's Liberation Movement 173-174
Writing: developing ideas, 94-97; pitching ideas,
    97-98; copy checking, 98-99; aims and objectives,
    99-101; interviewing 101-104; style and house
    style, 104; also see blogging

Y
YouTube 115